Also by Joseph Anthony Mazzeo

RENAISSANCE AND REVOLUTION:

The Remaking of European Thought

The Design of Life

Major Themes in the Development of Biological Thought

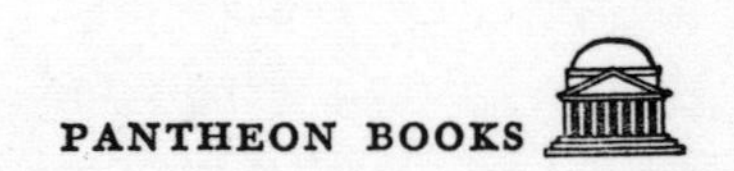

A Division of Random House | New York

The Design of Life

Major Themes in the Development of Biological Thought

by JOSEPH ANTHONY MAZZEO

First Printing

 Published in New York by Pantheon Books, a division of Random House, Inc., and simultaneously in Toronto, Canada, by Random House of Canada Limited.

Library of Congress Catalog Card Number: 67–19169

Manufactured in the United States of America
by The Book Press Incorporated, Brattleboro, Vermont.

PREFACE

A preface is usually the place where an author explains what he is up to or even apologizes for having presumed to write the book he has written. I will need to use this preface in both ways. The apology stems from the fact that this book is the outcome of an avocation. I am neither a professional biologist nor a professional historian of biology. It is thus the work of an amateur. That is not, I hope, necessarily or altogether a disadvantage. As the great historian Burckhardt remarked, amateurism is a downright liability only in the arts, where a certain perfection of execution is essential. In intellectual matters, it is sometimes an asset. It might, for instance, permit one to take a broader view of events and ideas, or to place familiar data in a fresh context. What is important, if amateurism is to be useful, is that the amateur be professional about *something*. Then he can bring some of the discipline and rigor of the professional to his avocational interest without the methods and procedures of professionalism.

The history of science, and the history of biology in particular, is a relatively new field of scholarly research. A great deal of specialized work needs to be done if the history of biology is to achieve the intellectual ripeness of, for example, the history of philosophy. Yet surely enough is known to make possible some coherent, brief account of the evolution of biological thought which will not be negated by future research. Unvexed by erudition, the amateur can make a useful contribution, even if of more modest import than the professional's.

My own professional experience in the humanities, and more specifically, in cultural history and the history of ideas as they apply to the elucidation of literature and philosophy, has given me a firm sense of what the history of a subject might be. From that standpoint, this book is most emphatically not a history. I have not attempted to be encyclopedic, to include every contribution of importance, or to take full and consistent account of the larger context of general history in which the history of biology unfolded. I have been guided in my selection of material by the major ideas of biological science, and my own professional bias will show in my emphasis on the interplay of biological ideas with each other and with ideas from other branches of knowledge.

I have therefore left out a good deal of material which might legitimately have been included. The reader will find only occasional discussion of the history of medicine in this book, and only insofar as medicine contributed to the growth of fundamental biological knowledge. The same is true of chemistry and physics. That a living organism can be studied as a chemical or physical system is a contribution of the first magnitude to biological science, but the details of that contribution are often of more concern to the scientist than to the historian of ideas. Nevertheless, the history of biology is unintelligible without reference to other fields of thought. The history of any branch of thought is really the history of problems. Biology, like any science, can easily be understood historically as a sequence of problems, and all of the great problems of science required the contributions of more than one branch of science for their solution. Modern genetics, for example, has drawn heavily on mathematics and biochemistry, to mention just two of the ancillary disciplines required to understand the facts about heredity. From another point of view, many of the crucial problems have not in any final sense been solved, but rather reformulated and raised to a higher level. We are still asking some of the same questions Aristotle asked when observing the developing embryo, although we have a lot more knowledge of biological phenomena to guide us. Problems persist, although men never deal with them twice in the same way in science. Sciences are, after all, special methods of research appropriate to particular problems. Indeed, if pursued too much in isolation, a science can easily degenerate into a narrow technical skill. The historian, in a manner analogous to the investigator himself, must avoid isolation and hold the problem before him as if it reverberated in many directions. He must show what ideas, techniques and instruments were applied at a certain time to take the solution of a problem a step further. Optics, painting, chemistry, physics, technological demands and creations, philosophical and religious ideas, all at one time or another have had a part to play in the evolution of biological thought, and sometimes in novel, improbable and oblique ways.

The unhistorical picture that so many scientists as well as laymen have of science has led to a strangely distorted view of what the life of the mind is really like. Science would seem to be nothing but a long series of cumulative conquests. Today's truth becomes tomorrow's error and there is a straight line leading from the errors of the past to the truth of today. As Eric Larrabee has argued,* many scientists simply cannot put themselves on any kind of equal footing with their intellectual ancestors. They do not know what the historian knows, that history, even the history of science, did not have to happen the way it did. This view, still too widespread among both laymen and scientists, is not unlike that of the "hardheaded" empiricist, whether he calls himself a businessman or a legislator or an economist. All such men appeal to "common sense," but as the great economist Keynes long ago pointed out, these tough-

* "Science and the Common Reader," *Commentary*, June, 1966.

minded empiricists are usually echoing the opinions of some theorist who lived before them and of whom they may not even have heard. The life of science is finally the life of ideas, and that is a dramatic life: the bold ideas of yesterday become the common sense of today; ideas are revived and found to be useful after having been neatly buried; the wrong side of some great scientific controversy in the past may have glimpsed a truth; a brilliant observation or experiment may lead to an erroneous but nevertheless fruitful hypothesis; a great discovery or invention may precede any thorough account of its intellectual significance; a major contribution may be ignored because it does not fit into the general scheme of scientific thought prevailing at the time.

These are some of the themes I have tried to touch on in my book. The order in which I deal with the major problems of biology is neither exclusively chronological nor exclusively thematic but something of a mixture of both. If my point of view, whatever its limitations, serves to stimulate interest in the study of biology or its history, this book will have served its purpose.

J. A. M.

CONTENTS

INTRODUCTION

Two profound and universal human characteristics lie behind the origin and growth of science: the need to control the workings of nature for our welfare and the simple, irreducible need to understand the world about us and ourselves. We today are sometimes inclined to draw too sharp a distinction between these two attitudes toward the world, the one practical and utilitarian, the other theoretical and contemplative, and to talk of "pure research" as something quite distinct from "applied science." Yet in the history of science, both motives for inquiry have been operative, sometimes apart and sometimes together. The great progress in astronomy during the seventeenth century was, at least to some degree, prompted by the needs of the art of navigation, much biological knowledge of a fundamental kind originated in man's search for ways to conquer illness, and the greatest contributions of Louis Pasteur to science came about as a result of his interest in problems of a very mundane kind, such as what made wine turn sour or what could be done about a plague that was destroying the silkworms of France. On the other hand, many investigators had little concern with the possible utility of their work in spite of the fact that a good deal of scientific research which seemed to have no possible practical outcome at first proved to be extremely useful later on.

Man has various ways of understanding the world. Certainly religion, art, literature, history and philosophy arise out of the attempt to understand and give an account of the world about us and ourselves, to specify the unknown, and to diminish both the mystery and the burden of existence. By means of magic, the magical uses of religion and art, ritual, or hit-or-miss methods, mankind has also tried to control nature. Often enough, useful knowledge and magic were mixed up together. Some of the Indians of North America would accompany the planting of corn with elaborate prayers and rituals, but they made sure they buried a dead fish with the planted corn seeds. Indians of South America treated malaria with a tea brewed from the bark of the cinchona tree, which does in fact contain an effective agent, quinine, until recent times the only treatment for this disease, but they knew no more about the causes of disease than their North American relatives knew about the nitrogen cycle. Nevertheless primitive peoples, including our own remote ancestors, made substantial progress in learning enough about nature to help themselves manage it, although their understanding of what they were doing was confined to myth. It is chastening for us to realize, however, that fire, the wheel, the domestication of animals, agriculture and other discoveries or inventions of the first importance were made by prehistoric man.

How then does science differ from traditional "know-how"? This might at first seem an easy question to answer, but it turns out to be quite complicated before long. We might say, in the light of my examples, that science gives a rational account of why things happen, that it is based on experience derived from observation, that once we know the causes of things we can predict what will happen, and other things of this sort. Yet science can be divided into a large number of activities which differ markedly from one another: the methods and techniques of the physicist are quite different from those of the biologist, those of the anthropologist quite different from those of the chemist.

A definition which includes all the activities we call science will have to be, as philosophers say, on a very high level of abstraction, and will tell us little about any of the particular sciences we are interested in. Still, that is a good place from which to begin and then work our way down to the biological sciences. We might think of science, in the first instance, as made up of bodies of knowledge about the natural world and about ourselves as part of nature. These bodies of knowledge, moreover, are systematically organized and derived entirely from observation and experimentation. Scientific knowledge is the sort of knowledge which, in principle and often in fact, allows us to predict specific events and control them. It is, finally, the sort of knowledge open to verification by others.

A philosophically sophisticated reader might take exception to this rough definition, but it does point to some of the features of scientific knowledge which mark it off from other kinds. The object of science is the understanding of natural phenomena. Science appeals to observation and experimentation as its marks of truth, and it is so stated that it is open to verification by others, through repeating either the observations or the experiments in question. It is systematically organized in that it is not simply an accumulation of facts, but of facts brought into a coherent and meaningful relation to one another. It aims, ideally, at prediction and control.

Theory, of course, plays an indispensable role in the progress of science and enters when we try to explain the significance of our observations or to determine what must be true about the nature of things if our observations are to be given some sort of intelligible explanation. Atoms, genes and many other crucial entities of scientific thought were postulated long before there was any weighty evidence for their physical existence or any definite knowledge of what they might be like if they did exist. John Dalton's chemical atoms had little to be said in their favor in the opinion of some of his contemporaries, and when Thomas

Hunt Morgan embarked on his long series of experiments in genetics, his assumption that the units of heredity, the genes, were physical entities went well beyond the then available evidence. But this only shows that a good theory should do more than explain what we know or systematize it for us. It should spur us to venture beyond the facts we have to new facts, new observations, new experiments which may confirm our theory or force us to modify it. We shall have occasion to consider a number of illuminating examples of the complex role that theory played in the history of biology.

I have already indicated that there is no one scientific method. Discoveries have been made in various ways and the methods suitable for one kind of study may be quite inappropriate to another. We should also distinguish between the account a rigorous logician will give of scientific method and the actual procedure of the scientist with all of the trials and errors, guesses, and psychological obscurities that may involve. A philosophically rigorous account of various methods in science may offer few if any clues to the psychology of scientific discovery, the inspired guesses, the imaginative leaps, the patient inquiries and investigations, which naturally interest the historian. It is the latter's job to try to "see it the way it was" and take account of the total context in which discoveries were made. We may thus have some occasion to consider how often notions that we can only regard as superstitious or archaic coexisted comfortably with brilliant ideas in the head of some great biologist. This should not surprise us too much. The great scientists were, often enough, people of complex personalities—at least as complex as ours—and it is just as difficult to ignore what seems to be the extravagant or absurd side of their minds as it is that of our own. Original minds in the history of thought quite often feel their way to fresh thought by routes which outsiders might consider odd or unnecessary.

It might nevertheless be useful to invent a highly abstract model of a modern scientist and conjecture how he might go about his work. James B. Conant, in his stimulating book

Modern Science and Modern Man, suggests the following model:

> Recognize that an indeterminate situation exists. This is a conflicting or obscure situation demanding inquiry. Two, state the problem in specific terms. Three, formulate a working hypothesis. Four, devise a method of investigation by observation . . . or experimentation or both. Five, gather and record the testimony of "raw data." Six, transform these raw data into a statement having meaning and significance. Seven, arrive at an assertion which appears to be warranted. If the assertion is correct, predictions may be made from it. Eight, unify the warranted assertion, if it proves to be new knowledge in science, with the body of knowledge already established.*

We can see from this description that our hypothetical scientist uses both deductive and inductive modes of reasoning. Without going into the complexities of logical theory, this means that he draws general conclusions from specific data, on the one hand, and on the other uses general ideas to infer some probable fact or event which he will be able to observe or verify. Thus Einstein's special theory of relativity was based on a large body of observation, experimentation and thought about the physical universe. His general conclusions from this body of knowledge, his theory, in turn encouraged scientists to look for new data which the theory maintained would exist. Such data were found and, to that degree, Einstein's deductions from his theory were verified.

Our hypothetical scientist, however, has made certain unacknowledged assumptions about the world before he even thought about method or began to investigate a problem. One of these assumptions is that the universe is real. This may seem so obvious to us that it scarcely needs to be mentioned. Yet many philosophies and religions in the history of civilization, movements of great influence which shaped the lives of millions of people, have proclaimed the world available to the senses an illusion, and the effect of such a belief has often enough been to make scientific inquiry seem utterly worthless.

* New York, 1952, p. 20.

In what sense is the universe real for the scientist as scientist? It is real because it is something about which we can have knowledge, something in principle *intelligible,* no matter how difficult it may be to understand it. It is moreover assumed to be governed by regularities, by a system of cause and effect, however problematic these concepts may be to philosophers.

The term "biology" was first introduced at the very beginning of the nineteenth century to refer to the study of living things, and this definition seems adequate enough until we reflect that the study of living things may take us quite far into geology, into chemistry or physics, and indeed, in the case of man, into history, anthropology and psychology. Biological inquiry can thus be varied indeed, though for all practical purposes we can assume that we know the difference between a geologist and a biologist when we realize that the former may study fossils in order to find oil while the latter will study them to understand more about biological evolution.

One traditional way of subdividing biology is according to the organisms studied. Thus we have botanists, zoologists, and from a more specialized point of view, bacteriologists, entomologists and the like. This kind of specialization is testimony to the enormous variety of living things. From another point of view, biology can be divided according to general principles which cut across classes or organisms. Thus we have morphology, the study of the structure and form of living things, taxonomy, their classification and naming, physiology, the study of intraorganismic functions and processes, and ecology, the study of the relationship of organisms to their physical and biological environment. Any of the investigators so described might be doing pure or applied research and most of them would have recourse to both descriptive and experimental methods in their investigations.

Biology, like the other sciences, has antecedents lost in the distant past. As soon as man developed language he began to name the living things about him, and even the languages of primitive peoples give evidence often enough of a very sound conception of the biological relations between the plants and animals among which they live. Hunting, fishing, agriculture, folk medicine, all of these activities required a certain amount of knowledge about the characteristics and behavior of living things, no matter how mixed up sound knowledge was with error, magic or myth. Centuries of accumulated knowledge of this sort lay behind the ancient Greek beginnings of Western scientific thought.

The biologist too makes the large assumptions that all scientists make, about the reality and intelligibility of the world, but he makes some others peculiar to his own subject. What, from the standpoint of modern biology, are the most important working principles of biological inquiry? Perhaps the most important is the conviction that living organisms obey the laws of physics and chemistry. This principle was by no means universally accepted in the past and long stretches of the history of biology are filled with the conflicts between "mechanists," who thought that living matter was governed by exactly the same laws that govern inorganic matter, and "vitalists" of one kind or another, who argued that living things obeyed special laws of their own. The more naive vitalists even argued for an immaterial or spiritual factor of some kind as requisite for life.

In the light of modern physical and chemical knowledge this argument seems rather sterile, although it was of great historical importance and great names in the history of biology were to be found on both sides of the controversy. While mechanism was by far the more fruitful hypothesis, not all vitalists were by any means naive or benighted. The laws of eighteenth-century physics and chemistry did not, after all, explain some of the most important properties of living things. Many biologists today, without making any concessions to vitalism at all, would be prepared to agree that living matter displays unique properties. As the great physicist and philosopher Erwin Schrödinger expressed it in his remarkable essay *What Is Life?*:

> Living matter, while not eluding the "laws of physics" as established up to date, is likely to involve other "laws of physics"

> hitherto unknown, which, however, once they have been revealed, will form just as integral a part of this science as the former.*

It is reasonable to assume, then, that with the further development of new concepts and techniques, the unique properties of living matter will be quite as amenable to human understanding as what we already know about nonliving matter. Indeed, Schrödinger suggests that the biologist of the future may well make a contribution to the science of physics and thus repay some of the debt he has been incurring up until now.

A second working principle of modern biology goes back to its origins and has never been disputed. Biologists assume that a great deal can be learned about the workings of a whole organism or its structural units by a study of component parts. A great deal of recent progress in cell physiology has rested on elaborate techniques for isolating the component parts of cells. Cell physiologists assume that the parts studied in isolation will give important, if not complete, information on how these parts work in the living cell. This may scarcely seem like a very risky assumption to make, but one can never be absolutely sure at first that the components of a living system will preserve their essential properties outside the system itself. In general, such problems as these have proved capable of solution, and this principle has amply proved its value.

A third assumption is common to all experimental sciences, and that is that the experiment you are performing does not change what you are trying to study, at least not in unpredictable ways. This may sound easy, but there are instances where it is very difficult to be aware of the effect of all the experimental conditions, and there are circumstances, at least in physics, in which it is impossible not to interfere with the very conditions you are trying to learn about. Most of the time, however, with care and skill, such difficulties are not insuperable.

A final working assumption is that similar organisms or parts of organisms can be expected to have equally similar prop-

* New York, 1945, pp. 68–69.

erties. It is clear that a good deal of medical research has depended on this assumption, and in general it has proved true that the results of work with appropriate experimental animals have been applicable to human beings. This is a special case of the very important problem of finding the right organism for learning what you want to know. It is astonishing how much biological and medical knowledge of fundamental importance has come from the study of relatively few organisms, and not just rats and guinea pigs. Modern genetics was largely developed through the study of the fruit fly, *Drosophila,* and sea urchins' eggs still seem to be choice material for cytologists. We shall consider later how important such choices are and the combination of scientific acumen and luck which goes into making them.

It is obvious that all of the principles and assumptions we have been considering are methodological principles for solving problems. What, then, from the point of view of modern biology, are the outstanding problems? The first one we might think about is the problem of development. How does the individual develop from the egg? How do the extraordinary metamorphoses of living things occur? How can living things change so much and still retain their identity? Development, some modern biologists would say, is *the* central problem of biology. It is certainly the oldest; Aristotle asked these questions and made outstanding contributions to the study of developmental biology. It is astonishing to realize that we know very little more about the fundamental problems of developmental biology than he did. The processes involved in differentiation of tissues, organogenesis, morphogenesis, the mechanisms of self-regulation in living things, are enormously complex, but they are among the most exciting problems of current biological research.

From the beginnings of scientific thought men have wondered about the material basis of life. What kind of stuff is a living thing made of? Is it a single substance or a mixture of one kind or another? Until the development of modern chemistry the answers to this question were necessarily crude. Greek thought never went beyond the theory of four elements, fire, water, earth and air, and their corresponding biological counterparts, the four humors, blood, phlegm, black bile and yellow bile. In this field modern progress has been spectacular, and the elucidation of the relationships between the chemical materials which make up the body, even the single cell, has been among the most brilliant accomplishments of the last few decades of biological research.

A third persistent question which biologists have asked has to do with the fact that life is characterized by growth, movement, activity of one kind or another. The first theories about the nature of this activity involved appeals to a "vital force" or to an immaterial principle of movement like a "soul." With the development of modern physics and chemistry, all questions about such phenomena were reformulated in terms of the laws governing the transformations of energy. How do living things convert one form of energy into another, and with such remarkable efficiency? The study of the energy relationships of living things is another of the most important fields of fundamental biological research in our time.

In biochemistry, in the study of energy relationships, and even to a large degree in the study of development, an ancient Greek biologist brought to life would find himself on very unfamiliar ground. He would recognize the questions, all right, but he would find both the answers we have and the hypotheses which guide our research very unfamiliar indeed. He would, however, be pretty much at home in two areas of contemporary biological interest: ethology, the study of animal behavior, and ecology, the study of the organism in its relationship to its environment. He could soon learn enough about genetics and evolution to get right to work in these fields, where even the modern investigator finds himself often enough in the situation of Aristotle. The progress of many fields of biology has depended on complex and elaborate instrumentation and techniques, but here the investigator is not infrequently left with little beyond a well-stocked mind, imagination, and very sharp eyes.

Karl von Frisch's study of the language of bees, the extraordinary dances the worker bee uses to communicate the location of food to other workers, Konrad Lorenz's observations on imprinting in geese, these important researches required little or no equipment. Perhaps even in other fields of biology some binding solutions to biological problems may still be found with simple equipment and careful thought and observation. Instruments and well-furnished laboratories are often utterly indispensable, but even the most elaborate instrumentation will only help you get information. What makes a man a biologist is how he thinks about what he sees, whether with the naked eye or with an electron microscope. The history of biology may give us some insight into what biological thinking has been like.

The Design of Life

Major Themes in the Development of Biological Thought

i *Greek Biology*

Ancient science, on a thoroughly rationalistic basis, began about six hundred years B.C. in Ionia, that part of the Greek world which lay on the Aegean coast of what is now Turkey. At least, the records we have make that date as plausible as such dates can be. Ionia was a cosmopolitan part of the Hellenic world, exposed to influences from the civilizations which lay to the east, and situated as it was on the coastal trade routes which circled the whole of the Mediterranean, it was also continually visited by foreigners of different habits and speech. Cultural interaction has always seemed to sharpen men's wits, calling into question their traditional beliefs and values, so it is perhaps to be expected that philosophy, as an attempt to give a rational account of the world, should have begun, for Western civilization in any case, at the Asiatic frontier of ancient Greece.

The first of these early philosophers of whom we have notice is Thales (640?–546? B.C.), and he and his successors, Anaximander, Empedocles and others, gave us our first accounts of the world in terms of natural principles and general laws. The little that we know of their work may seem primitive to us today, but they have the great merit of ignoring or at least minimizing the possible role of the supernatural in natural phenomena. They sought to find what is permanent, regular and abiding in the midst of change and variety, whether a fundamental substance or a fundamental law, and this impulse is recognizable as the very root of scientific inquiry.

Man had possessed from prehistoric times a considerable amount of practical biological knowledge which he employed in agriculture, hunting and fishing, the activities necessary to sustain life, but it was perhaps illness more than anything else that urged him to deepen his knowledge of the nature of living things. The first man whom, to our definite knowledge, made systematic biological investigations was Alcmaeon (fl. 500 B.C.), a Greek from Croton in southern Italy. His extensive dissections of animals and his careful study of the development of the chick embryo were probably motivated by both medical and biological interests. His skill as a dissector must have been considerable, for he described the nerves of the eye and discovered the Eustachian tube which connects the middle ear with the throat, a discovery that was forgotten and then made all over again more than two thousand years later by the Italian anatomist Bartolomeo Eustachi, after whom the tube is named.

It seems clear from the scanty records available that Alcmaeon was not alone in his investigations, and there is little doubt that a continuous tradition of biological or medical study descends from his time to the time of Hippocrates (460?–377? B.C.), the first great figure in the history of Greek biology whose writings we possess. He was so eminent a physician and filled his disciples with such respect and reverence that they put his name on their own treatises. Thus a fair amount of the work attributed to Hippocrates is certainly not from his hand, although it seems clear that it reflects his thinking on medical subjects in a trustworthy manner.

Biology and medicine have always been intimately related, although their histories are by no means parallel. In addition to many contributions to the art of medicine in a restricted sense, Hippocrates made a contribution of the first importance to both medicine and biology: he gave an uncompromisingly naturalistic account of illness as a strictly biological phenomenon. In a Hippocratic treatise on epilepsy, *On the Sacred Disease*, so called because the sufferer was thought to be possessed by a god during his seizure, we find a total rejection of any supernatural agency as the cause of epileptic attacks. Epilepsy, the author tells us, has natural causes, even if we are ignorant of precisely what they are, and those who blame it on one god or another are simply superstitious and are trying to hide their own ignorance. Illness is a natural biological fact, not a mysterious event, however little knowledge we have about it.

The Hippocratic physicians not only postulated a natural origin for all illness, they also worked out a general theory of the causes of illness based on their notions of physiological function. The liquid part of the body, they believed, was composed of four substances, blood, phlegm, black bile and yellow bile. These substances, or "humors," were in turn derived from the four fundamental "elements" which were presumed to constitute, in varying proportions, all material things, living or not: fire, water, earth and air. These elements could under certain conditions change into one another, but they were the basic stuff of the universe and not reducible to anything simpler. Each element, however, was a unity of two of the four primary qualities, of heat, cold, moisture and dryness: fire was hot and dry, water cold and wet, earth cold and dry, air hot and wet. In a derivative way these qualities were present in the physiological "humors," which was why an excess of one humor would give you a fever or the excess of another a chill. In fact, a man became ill precisely because he had an imbalance of humors, although even in the healthy state he might have a predominance of one humor or another. This normal predominance accounted for his prevailing temperament, so that the melancholy temperament had a little too much black bile ("melancholy" means black bile in Greek), the man of cheerful outlook had a little more blood than others and so was "sanguine" (from the Latin for blood), the man with a preponderance of phlegm in his normal constitution was "phlegmatic," and so on. If these normal preponderances became excessive, a man became ill. It is clear that this theory, which lasted until well into the modern era, is both a theory of disease and a theory of personality. It lasted so long that we can easily understand how it became so deeply embedded in our vocabulary for describing personality types.

How then was a disease to be cured? The answer the Hippocratic physicians gave is still an important one: the body cures itself. If a patient is given proper diet and enough rest, and if attention is given to his personal cleanliness, self-regulative mechanisms will come into play which will restore his physiological balance and so his health. In this sense, nature and not the physician does the healing, for the body itself possesses the only healing powers there really are. These ideas came to be expressed in two Latin phrases famous in the history of medicine, *vis medicatrix naturae,* "the healing power of nature," and *natura sanat non medicus,* "nature and not the physician heals." The Hippocratic theory, however primitive the physiology and chemistry on which it rests, has some truth tucked away in it. In fact, Hippocrates advanced the theory of disease as a breakdown in "homeostasis," or internal physiological balance, and there is no doubt that a good many functional disorders are now so understood in principle. Moreover, with important qualifications, it is still true to say that in the last analysis, the body does heal itself, although we now have many ways of helping it do so. In view of the drastic treatments with which the history of medicine abounds, for many centuries one's best chance for not being made sicker lay in going to a physician of Hippocratic training and ideals. If he used drugs at all, they were likely to be simple herbs which at worst did little harm.

The scientific spirit in which the Hippocratic physicians approached illness is also manifest in their meticulous descriptions of the course of various illnesses; the Hippocratic description of tuberculosis is still considered a masterpiece of clinical observation. If they could do little for many of their patients, they at least did them little harm. Even with our vast array of drugs and medical procedures, the conviction that it is nature that heals and that the physician can only help is still a vital principle of sound medical practice.

Biology as the study of living things simply for the sake of understanding them, and as a considerable body of organized knowledge about them, begins with the work of Aristotle (384–322 B.C.). Obviously he had predecessors, in medicine especially, who prepared the way for his monumental labors, but he stands to his predecessors, of whom we know something if not a great deal, as Darwin stands to the whole previous history of modern biology. Darwin himself, as well as more recent biologists of distinction such as Sir D'Arcy Thompson and Joseph Needham, called him the greatest biologist of all time. This accolade may strike us as odd, at first. Aristotle knew nothing of evolution or genetics, he had no microscope, no knowledge of chemistry (a lack which severely limited his physiological speculations), nothing, in fact, but his mind and his eyes. What marks Aristotle's greatness is precisely his remarkable powers of observation and an astounding ability to interpret what he saw in the light of principles of biological reasoning which are still fresh and of fundamental importance. His conception of taxonomy, his formulation of morphological and developmental problems, his extraordinary studies in embryology—perhaps his scientific masterpiece—and his brilliant grasp of ecological problems, of the relation of living things to their physical and biological environment: these are among his contributions of enduring importance.

Part of the adverse criticism of Aristotle which one occasionally encounters, in some of the older histories of science especially, is based on a confusion of his thought with that of some of his followers, the Aristotelians, who in many cases obscured what he actually thought. But a greater part is based on a direct misunderstanding of what he did think. He has, for example, been roundly denounced in some quarters as a "teleologist," as holding to the notion that all living things and organic structures have a purpose and are guided toward a final end or goal of development by some inner impulse. And he does, in fact, insist that nature makes the organ for its function and not the function for the organ, the reverse of the Darwinian conception of structures achieving their function through the operation of natural selection on random variations. To this degree it is true that Aristotle adhered to teleological notions, but we should be aware that he was not nearly as naive about those notions as some of his critics think. He often talks "teleology" where we would talk "adaptation," and he expressly denies that living things realize "purposes" in anything like the way human beings do. When, in his biological work, he talks of the final end or "cause" of the acorn being an oak, he is simply talking like a functionalist and means little more than we do when we ask what the purpose of the heart is, or when we refer to embryological development as a "directed process." Moreover, as Needham has pointed out, he knew how to nod toward his teleological notions and "press on with the dissection." He was, in short, flexible and sophisticated in his use of teleological assumptions and about other theories as well. His works show frequent modifications of thought on a subject in the light of new evidence, and we hear in him the voice of the true investigator of nature when he tells us that theories must yield to observation and that one should believe a theory only when it agrees with the observed facts.

Aristotle's methodological analysis of principles of taxonomic classification, remarkable for its thoroughness and subtlety, is still unsurpassed in philosophic richness. He rejected right off, for example, the possibility of a simple dichotomous classification of species and explained why such a system would turn into a biological hodgepodge. If one divided living creatures, for instance, into those with wings and those without wings—a plausible notion at first glance—one would class many insects with birds but separate winged and wingless ants into two utterly distinguished categories. Aristotle grasped that the only workable system of classification for animals would have to be based on their body plan, and that it would employ more than a simple twofold division. His distinction between animals with blood and animals without blood, roughly comparable to our vertebrates and invertebrates, is based on a radical difference in body plan with the circulatory system as the key structure. Moreover, he conceived of the diversity of living things as arranged in a taxonomic hierarchy or ladder instead of in random kinds of order. We still use this model of order in taxonomy, although we do not think of this "ladder of creatures" as timeless or unchanging, nor do we feel, as Aristotle did, that creatures higher up the ladder are in some sense more "perfect" than creatures lower down.

Aristotle also advanced the principle which has since come to be known as the principle of the correlation of parts, the idea that organs are interrelated in very particular ways which determine their size and structure, so that the development of one organ, for example, leads to the reduction of another. Thus, he pointed out that a mammal with horns would have fewer teeth than one without horns, and he believed that this type of correlation was based on the limited amount of horn- and tooth-like substance the animal could generate. Other kinds of correlation were more functional in character. His best work in this regard was with birds, and he noted how the particular architectural relations between the parts of a bird not only demonstrated internal correlations of parts but were further correlated to the bird's behavior and its particular dealings with the environment.

Behind Aristotle's morphological reasoning lay the principle of the economy of nature, the notion that nature is "parsimonious," that it does nothing in vain and uses the smallest number of means to achieve its end. This may sound a little anthropomorphic, but with the appropriate qualifications and expansions it is still a principle of some importance in scientific thought. We might say today that natural processes occur with no unnecessary expenditure of energy, that an organism will have the simplest possible structure for proper functioning in its particular environment. This is after all the explanatory principle we use when we postulate that a species which takes up a parasitic mode of existence comes to lose structures and functions that its free-living ancestors possessed.

Aristotle's biological investigations are everywhere marked by continual attention to both structure and function. These were, for him, two sides of the same coin. A structure is the way it is because of its function, and a particular function requires a specific structure for its realization. As we have seen, he applied this way of thinking not only to the internal organization of an organism but to its relation to the environment as well. Aristotle was not an evolutionist—nor was anyone else at his time and for a long time thereafter—but in his own way he was as thoroughly impressed with the adaptedness of life as was Darwin, even if he lacked any conception of adaptation as the result of a historical process in which species are transformed through selection. His marvelous eye for structure permitted him, even without a microscope, to distinguish between tissues and organs. He discerned that some parts of the body were, as he put it, "homogeneous" while others were composed of heterogeneous parts and were therefore "nonhomogeneous."

Perhaps the most important biological principle Aristotle introduced was the distinction between homologous and analogous body parts in organisms of different species. Thus the foot of a man and the paw of a dog are homologous in that they possess a similar architecture, while the claw of a lobster and the hand of a man are analogous because, although they both can grasp something, they are constructed on entirely different principles. In our own time these concepts have acquired a new significance in terms of evolutionary relationships, but this seemingly simple distinction is the basis for any scientific comparison between the anatomy of different organisms, even prescinding from their evolutionary relationships. Homologous parts perform the same or similar functions, and they are constructed in the same or nearly the same way. Analogous parts have the same or similar functions, but they are constructed in totally different ways. As Aristotle perceived, nature has more than one way of doing the same thing, and without a sure grasp of the principles of homology and analogy we can have no notion of what the resemblances between organisms might signify.

In embryology Aristotle was a convinced upholder of epigenesis, the theory that the embryo develops from a relatively simple and undifferentiated state into a complex individual by interaction among its simple parts or constituents. His observations in this field were unsurpassed until the Renaissance, and his analysis and interpretation of the events of embryogenesis raise all of the most important questions of developmental biology. Aristotle asked, as every embryologist must, why the egg of a particular species develops into the individual of that species and no other. Adherents of preformation, the notion that the embryo exists from the beginning as a kind of miniature adult with all of its parts completely developed although on a very small scale, have also been concerned to explain the reproductive continuity of the species, perhaps more concerned than the proponents of epigenesis. That was perhaps the reason why they felt compelled to postulate some concrete kind of preformation even in the absence of palpable evidence. Whether by design or by chance, Aristotle avoided being trapped by that problem into making any assumptions about preformation which would contradict the evidence of his senses. Whatever principle determined the development of the embryo into the individual of its species, it was "invisible," some sort of molding power resident in the semen which shaped the embryo as a sculptor shapes a stone. This idea did not really explain very much, but it permitted Aristotle to reconcile the abundant evidence that no structures are preformed with due acknowledgment of the fact that some mechanism must exist which directs embryonic development in a specific way.

It is interesting that in the seventeenth century, Marcello Malpighi (1629–1694), a magnificent observer and one of the greatest of the early microscopists, gave meticulous and accurate "epigenetical" descriptions of the development of the hen's egg. Nevertheless, he adhered in some degree to preformation of a kind at the same time that he took due account of epigenesis. It seemed required by theoretical necessity, and it is probable that Malpighi's crude microscope led him to note sufficient complexity of structure in the earliest embryo to assume that what he saw were structured prototypes of organs. He confirmed all of the most crucial observations Aristotle made, that general structures appear in the embryo before more specialized ones and that "homogeneous" parts appear before "nonhomogeneous" parts.

On questions of heredity Aristotle knew as much as anyone, including Charles Darwin, up until the work of Mendel. Perhaps nowhere else in Aristotle's work do we get a more brilliant example of good reasoning in theoretical biology than in his criticism of the theory of heredity identified with the Hippocratic school. This theory, that of pangenesis, was to be revived in its essentials by Darwin, and Aristotle's criticism applies to Darwin's version as well as to the Hippocratic one. As we shall see, Darwin elaborated the earlier version of the theory to take account of some of Aristotle's objections, but not with complete success.

The theory of pangenesis maintains that the entire organism, in a sense, reproduces itself. Tiny particles are continually being produced in all parts of the body, particles which correspond to the differences between these parts. They continually migrate into the semen. After insemination, these particles congregate with their likes and form the complete embryo which then grows in size. In the Hippocratic theory both male and female contributed the stuff of heredity, there being both a male and a female semen or seed. (Darwin also allowed an equal role to the female as a contributor of pangenes, or "gemmules," as he called the tiny particles, to the embryo.)

Aristotle maintained that the facts of heredity could not be accounted for with such a theory. The proponents of pangenesis argued—as indeed did Darwin—that the pangenes continually being produced would reflect the state of the parent at the time of conception, so that weak parents, for example, would produce weak offspring. Aristotle pointed out that parents whose hair is not grey at the time of fertilization, or a father who is beardless when he conceives a son, will nevertheless produce offspring who in due course will have grey hair, or a son who will eventually be able to grow a beard. Even in plants and most certainly in animals, the offspring can and do develop characteristics which the parents did not have at the time of their conception.

If the pangenes reflect the state of the parental body at the moment of conception, how would this be possible?

In addition, Aristotle argued, children sometimes resemble grandparents and not their parents, and such children could not possibly have received particles from their grandparents by the direct transmission postulated by the Hippocratic school. Nor do the children of mutilated or crippled parents often, if ever, inherit their parents' deformities. This would necessarily occur if pangenes were accurate reflectors of the state of the body parts from which they originated. Aristotle is less convincing to us when he argues that the embryo is not intimately connected with the body that contains it, perhaps on the analogy with avian or reptilian eggs which do develop outside the mother, and that he therefore sees no plausible way for it to accrete pangenes which might be required for its growth. It seemed to him no more likely that this could happen than that particles from clothing and shoes should enter the semen of the parent!

It was widely held by medical thinkers in Aristotle's time that the sex of the embryo was determined by chance. Against such a notion, Aristotle's theory of fertilization provides a specific mechanism for sex determination. Unlike the Hippocratics and those influenced by them, Aristotle denied that there was a female "seed." What the female contributed was a "matter," the menstrual blood, which fused with the male semen carrying the principle of "form." Upon fusion there was a "coagulation" which was the earliest embryo, quite undifferentiated and not preformed as the embryo would really have to be according to theories of pangenesis. In spite of its simplicity, the sex of the embryo was determined potentially at this moment of coagulation (fertilization, we would say) according to whether the female or male contribution to the embryo was dominant. We should not assume, by the way, that when Aristotle speaks of the semen as conferring "form" he is dematerializing the father's contribution to the embryo. Form in Aristotle's meaning is precisely the principle which confers a particular reality on things and makes them what they are. All things in the natural world are compounds of matter, their possibilities, we might say, and form, that which realizes and defines those possibilities.

Aristotle was by no means solely a great theoretician. His thinking was rooted in the study of many specimens, in careful dissections, and in prolonged observation of the living organism in its natural habitat. He made some errors, but the best of his descriptions of organisms and their behavior were not equaled for centuries. He traveled much and little escaped his inquiring mind and keen eyes.

Although Aristotle founded a school, the Lyceum, he left only one important pupil who carried on his scientific investigations, Theophrastus (c.372–c.287 B.C.), a botanist who evidently tried to complete his master's work by studying plants as intensively as Aristotle had studied animals. His remaining botanical works are not marked by any great brilliance, but the account of germination in his *History of Plants* ("history" here means, as it does in all translations of ancient scientific works, "inquiry into") is the best of its kind until the work of Malpighi in the seventeenth century.

In general Theophrastus does not rise very much above the descriptive level, but he did recognize the existence of sexuality in plants, as did others for centuries after him, though the actual distinction between the male and female parts of plants eluded him—as, indeed, it eluded everyone else until modern times. If the contributions of Aristotle remind us of how much was accomplished in biology a long time ago, Theophrastus reminds us of how recent much of our fundamental knowledge of living things is. A careful study of sexuality in plants was not soberly and lucidly presented until the work of a German professor of botany, Rudolf Jakob Camerarius (1665–1721). His remarkable insights into the role of insects in plant fertilization were not extensively developed until many years later by Christian Konrad Sprengel (1750–1816), and the actual fertilization of a plant was not observed until 1830 by the Italian microscopist Giovanni Battista Amici.

In one instance involving sexuality in plants, Theophrastus was right: that of the date palm, where the male and female organs are on different plants and where artificial fertilization had been practiced from time immemorial throughout the Near East and North Africa. Interestingly enough, this fact, which might well have served as a good point of departure for the study of plant sexuality, was lost sight of until the Renaissance, when it was rediscovered by Prospero Alpini (1553–1617), who also had the distinction of being the first European to describe the coffee plant.

Alexander the Great (356–323 B.C.), a more famous but distinctly unscientific pupil of Aristotle, conquered in his short life a vast empire and took Greek culture into North Africa, the Near East and even as far as the Indus Valley. To unify his great polyglot empire and to memorialize his conquests, he founded a new city in Egypt, Alexandria. He did not live to govern long, and after his death, his empire was divided up among his generals. Alexandria and Egypt passed to his general Ptolemy, who founded the dynasty named after him, the Ptolemies. They were to rule Egypt for nearly three hundred years, until the death of Cleopatra, the last of the dynasty.

This dynasty founded and maintained the most famous institution of learning in the ancient world, the Museum of Alexandria. This name is a little misleading to us in the present day, for the Alexandrian Museum was more like a great graduate school and center of research than like a modern museum. This name was given to it because the nine Muses of Greek mythology presided over the various branches of learning as well as the arts, and so symbolized the fact that all the branches of learning were cultivated at the Museum, literary and historical scholarship, philosophy, mathematics, music, physics, biology, astronomy and medicine.

Much of the vast production of generations of scholars who worked at the Museum was lost, and the two greatest names in biology from this period survive only in fragments. They were the anatomist Herophilus (fl. 300 B.C.) and his near contemporary the physiologist Erasistratus (fl. 250 B.C.). Herophilus made a considerable number of anatomical investigations, careful studies of the eye, liver, spleen and reproductive system, and distinguished between the motor and sensory nerves. He surmised, no doubt on the basis of his study of the nervous system, that the brain was the seat of intelligence. Previous opinion had located the seat of intelligence in the heart, probably because of its obvious activity, its sensitivity to variations in our emotional state, and the fact that consciousness ends with the cessation of heart action. Herophilus was also the first to note that the pulse is located in the arteries and not the veins.

Erasistratus based his physiology on the notion that every organ is made up of three kinds of vessels, veins, arteries and nerves, the last thought at that time and for many centuries after to be hollow and to carry a fluid. He was especially interested in the brain, and to him we owe the knowledge of the distinction between the cerebrum and the cerebellum as well as the notion that the more numerous convolutions of the human brain as compared with animal brains were related to man's greater intelligence. We still believe this today, but have no more precise idea than did Erasistratus of just why it should be so.

About 200 B.C. Greek science entered on a decline, and this is in some respects a puzzling historical problem. Ancient civilization was to remain vital for several centuries, during which there were great achievements in other branches of human endeavor, intellectual as well as practical, so the decline in science was not part of a general process of decay. Historians have advanced a number of explanations for this phenomenon. Some think that the failure to cultivate technology and practical applications of scientific knowledge on any large scale deprived science of an important stimulus to research. More important, this lack of a sense of the utilitarian side of scientific research left science unrelated to the needs of society as a whole and therefore deprived it of the support of important political and social leaders. Others note that the collapse of the small Greek city-states, the political and cultural heart of Greek civilization, and their eventual incorporation into great empires like that of Rome left men more uncertain of their place in the world and more unsure of their values, so that philosophers turned from the study of nature to the consideration of religious and ethical problems. In the view of one great classical scholar, Gilbert Murray, a "failure of nerve" gradually overtook Greek civilization and thoughtful men came to seek salvation of one kind or another rather than theoretical or practical knowledge. Still other historians blame the decline on the general failure of ancient civilization to diffuse an understanding of its highest cultural values, scientific or other, to enough of the population. The "base of support," so to speak, for an ongoing community of scholars and scientists was therefore lacking.

Whatever the causes for the decline of ancient science may be, it is certain that some special conditions seem to be required for the growth of science. Important civilizations have existed which made little contribution to science, so that civilization and science are not necessarily synonymous. Only in recent times has any extensive research been done on what we now call the "sociology of science" and the results of these inquiries are still quite tentative. It is clear, however, that the growth of science is intimately related to the values of a civilization, to the kinds of activity it considers important. It depends on the existence of social institutions whereby scientific knowledge and skills are accumulated and transmitted to future generations, and on a cooperating community of scientists who share their knowledge and train their successors. The leaders, at least, of a society must be willing to divert a portion of the general wealth to the support of these activities in the belief that they are of importance, both practically and culturally. It indicates an enormous cultural shift when at one time in the history of a culture philanthropists or governments spend their wealth on temples and at another time on centers of scholarship and research. Ancient civilization, in short, lacked the university and related institutions as we now conceive them, as well as a widely diffused and socially active sense of the importance of scientific knowledge to society at large. As the role of science in our society grows, both historical and contemporary studies of the relation of science to general cultural conditions should be of great utility in giving perspective to our social and political plans dependent upon or affected by science.

However gifted the Romans were as soldiers, statesmen, lawyers and administrators, they were not scientists nor were they especially curious about nature. The cultural spheres in which they achieved high excellence were literature, portrait sculpture and architecture. In scientific matters the Romans were derivative and fell well below the best of the Greek scientific thinkers. Although the great works of Greek thought were available to them, and educated Romans for centuries knew Greek well, the scientific works of the Greeks had little influence on Roman culture. The Romans scarcely assimilated them, much less used them as points of departure for fresh inquiry.

On the other hand, the Romans were excellent engineers, as we might expect from the practical bent of their genius. Their aqueducts, their roads, so necessary for military purposes, their sewers, even their household plumbing, were admirable technological accomplishments. But their utter lack of interest in theory and in the general principles of nature limited even the technological progress they might have achieved. If the Greeks were too little concerned with the practical consequences of science, the Romans were too little interested in that general knowledge of the properties of things on which technology, in the last analysis, must rest, if technological progress is not to be a matter of simple trial and error.

Educated Romans, if they were interested in science at all, usually got their scientific knowledge from digests and encyclopedias, and not from the magisterial texts of Greek science. Two well-known figures in providing this kind of intellectual fare were Aulus Cornelius Celsus (fl. A.D. 30) and Gaius Plinius Secundus (A.D. 23–79), known to posterity as Pliny. The medical portion of Celsus' work survived into the Middle Ages and, however inferior it was to the works of Hippocrates or Galen, it enjoyed a great deal of popularity precisely because it was such a simplified version of Greek medicine and so easily accessible to the untrained reader. It became, for those who could read, a kind of "do-it-yourself" medical text.

Pliny, an amateur and gentleman, compiled a large encyclopedia of natural history which enjoyed uninterrupted popularity into modern times. This long work is an unusual mixture of sound information and fantastic stories about "marvelous" creatures. It gives little evidence of first-hand observation and none at all of that critical intelligence which is so marked in the works of Aristotle. Nevertheless, Pliny was the major source in natural history for centuries. Agreeably written, it taxed the reader's intelligence to the smallest possible degree and was filled with the sort of biological marvels which have a popular appeal in any age. Pliny's work is strongly marked by an anthropocentric approach to the study of natural history, another reason for the wide and durable appeal of his book. Our fellow creatures, in Pliny's view, are not merely useful to man but were somehow designed to be useful to man: that is their very reason for being. Even their habits, real or fabulous, are meant to teach us ethical precepts or warn us of moral dangers. The bestiaries of the Middle Ages took many of their little animal sermons from Pliny, directly or indirectly, so when we are gratified to learn from a medieval bestiary that the pelican feeds its young with its own blood and that we should emulate its self-sacrificing character, we can discern the shadow of Pliny not far away.

Greek biology found two significant voices during the Roman period, in spite of the general decline, and both were physicians. The first, Dioscorides (fl. A.D. 60), was a military surgeon in the legions of the Emperor Nero. His work was not, as we might at first expect, medical in the strict sense of the term, but botanical. During the centuries after Hippocrates physicians turned more and more to the use of medication, and the ancient pharmacopoeia was almost entirely botanical. Dioscorides left descriptions of some six hundred species of plants together with medical information about them. Some manuscripts of his herbal are beautifully illustrated, even by modern standards. There was, in fact, a well-developed art of botanical drawing before and during his period, an art which had declined by the end of antiquity and was not recovered again until the Renaissance. Botanical illustrators apparently influenced artists in general, for Roman decorative sculpture has fine examples of precise renderings of plants and flowers.

Far more important and distinguished than Dioscorides was Galen (A.D. c.130–c.200), who even more than Hippocrates in many respects became the great medical authority until the seventeenth century. He was a remarkably voluminous writer, although a good deal of his work did not survive into modern times, and was especially interested in anatomy and physiology. It is not clear whether he ever dissected the human body, but it is certain that many of his descriptions intended to apply to the human body are really descriptions of the Barbary ape. His physiological investigations were focused on the functions of the spinal cord, lungs and heart. When we discuss the work of William Harvey, we shall have occasion to consider Galen's conception of the circulation of the blood in some detail. It was until Harvey's time the accepted account of the circulatory system.

Galen became such an authority in his time and afterward that his errors were hard to eliminate even after the widespread revival of direct anatomical observation in the Renaissance. Among the most influential of these was his notion that the air enters directly into the heart via the lungs and that the blood passes directly from one side of the heart to the other through the septum, the wall itself, by means of invisible pores. As we shall see, it took a great deal of effort to dislodge these errors even when the evidence was at hand that Galen must have been wrong.

One measure of the cultural distance between Galen and his greatest predecessor, Hippocrates, lies in their philosophical outlook. Although a pagan, Galen was a monotheist as many pagans were, especially those of Stoic philosophical outlook. In this he shared the same philosophical perspective as his famous client the Emperor Marcus Aurelius. Under the influence largely of Stoicism, Galen believed that God had created every organ in a perfect form to express a particular function. This function, moreover, reflected God's intention, as indeed did everything else in the natural universe. The laws which governed the universe were not simply laws of nature but a direct manifestation of the mind of God, his will and his intentions.

The human body, like all else, should be understood in the light of this precept.

Whereas the Hippocratic physicians had expressly refrained from invoking any supernatural causes or metaphysical speculations, Galen found food for his philosophical and religious ideas everywhere in the human organism. It would be misleading to suggest that Galen forced these notions wherever he could. He was a good observer and a thoughtful investigator. But as compared with the Hippocratic works, we find a great change in the intellectual atmosphere in Galen's work, and Galen with all his erudition reflects a time when if the study of nature were to go on at all, it went on tied to the ethical and religious concerns which dominated the intellectual life of later antiquity.

ii *The Fabric and Diversity of Life*

As classical civilization declined, a new civilization was slowly coming to birth, that of the Middle Ages. In the earlier part of the medieval period, the so-called "dark ages" from about the sixth to the ninth century, little remained alive of ancient culture. One invasion after another ravaged Europe. The European economy and social organization steadily declined, a decline which had actually begun well before the political collapse of the Roman Empire. Urban life practically disappeared from great stretches of Europe where it had once flourished. The loss of Asia and Africa to the great armies of Islam drastically diminished what European commerce still flourished from Roman times and reduced even further the sources of European wealth and the cultural stimulus which accompanies trade.

During the Dark Ages the conditions for learning of any kind, let alone scientific learning, were not favorable. Monastic and religious schools were the homes of what learning there was, and their obviously religious orientation was not, at that time, favorable to anything we could remotely call scientific inquiry. In Western Europe, Italy alone had preserved something reminiscent of ancient urban life and there alone was learning not entirely the monopoly of the clergy. A class of educated laymen, mostly lawyers, survived in some of the Italian cities throughout the medieval period. It was no accident that the great expansion of secular learning which marks the beginning of the Renaissance should have started in Italy.

By the twelfth century Europe had markedly recovered from its lowest point and had reversed the long process of devolution which began toward the end of antiquity. Cities, many of them taking their origins from the sites of trading fairs, increased in number and size. Strong rulers in the new rising nation states—England, France, Castile—established the conditions of security required for a rise in the level of life. Universities were founded and more and more men, students and teachers, began to seek for and recover the legacy of ancient culture.

Meanwhile, the Arabs had developed a great civilization of their own and had established their power in parts of Europe such as Spain and Sicily. They had conquered great sections of what had been the empire of Alexander and later of the Romans. Like their Roman predecessors in empire, they had gone to school with the Greek-speaking peoples who became their subjects. Arab scholars learned Greek, translated the works of Aristotle and other Greek thinkers, studied and interpreted them, and made further contributions using the Greek works as a foundation. At those points where Islamic culture touched Europe, where Christian, Arab and Jew came to know each other, Latin versions of the Arabic translations and commentaries were made. Europe, which for the most part had lost direct contact with its Hellenic legacy, began to recover it through a detour provided by Islam. Bit by bit Europeans recovered the ancient scientific legacy. They received a bonus as well, for Arab scholars had by this time made outstanding contributions to mathematics, optics and medicine. By the thirteenth century some European scholars had learned enough Greek to make fresh translations of Aristotle and other Greek texts directly from the original, and by the end of the thirteenth century just about all the works of Aristotle which are extant were available in more accurate versions than those made from Arabic translations.

A good many important developments in technology and agriculture took place during the Middle Ages, and European scholars made important contributions to mathematics and physics among the sciences, but biology and medicine languished. Although medical faculties soon appeared at the new universities, it was not until the thirteenth century that dissection was revived, at Bologna, the oldest of the European universities. Medical instruction was largely concerned with the study of texts such as those of Galen or of Arabic elaborations on Greek medicine such as the writings of Avicenna. Even when dissection was revived, it had little to do with making a fresh examination of the structure of the human body. The professor of anatomy lectured from one of the ancient texts while an inferior did the actual cutting up of the fast-decomposing cadaver. A physician was a member of the learned profession, and it was considered beneath his dignity for him to get his hands dirty messing around with corpses. Indeed, even surgery was too demeaning an activity for a physician, and for centuries surgery was usually the task of people like barbers. Such surgeons used harsh remedies, and it was not until the time of Ambroise Paré (c.1510–1590) that matters improved. Paré used gentle ointments on wounds instead of the usual disinfectant of boiling oil and stopped bleeding by tying off arteries instead of cauterizing them with hot irons. One familiar residue of the tradition of the barber-surgeon is the red and white striped barber's pole, which once signified the surgical side of his business. Even today in Great Britain surgeons are addressed as "Mister" instead of the once more prestigious title of "Doctor," although there is no trace left of the traditional snobbery associated with this distinction in forms of address.

The first man to break with the old tradition of teaching anatomy and do his own dissecting was a professor at the University of Bologna, Mondino de' Luzzi (1275–1326), who published a book on anatomy in 1316, the first new text in modern times. Unfortunately, his practice of making his own observations was not continued after his death and he left no successors.

The Renaissance has been variously defined as a revival of learning, as the rise of the middle class and of the culture peculiar to it, as the secularization of European civilization, and as the period in which modern social and political institutions first made their appearance. In fact, it is all of these in varying proportions and with certain qualifications applicable to different times and places. For the historian of biology, the biological renaissance does not begin with the recovery of the biological knowledge of antiquity. That, as we have seen, took place during the latter part of the Middle Ages. Rather the renaissance in biology begins with the recovery of the habit of direct observation as the primary source of biological knowledge. In the fifteenth and sixteenth centuries biological progress can largely be measured in two great fields of work which certainly require direct observation: natural history and anatomy.

Much of the stimulus for a renewed interest in direct observation of living things came from the great voyages of exploration and discovery. New animals, new plants, indeed, new human beings were introduced to Europeans. The diversity of life forced itself upon Europeans in an unprecedented fashion and no one at all interested in natural history could avoid a fresh confrontation with nature itself. One of the great names in the revival of natural history is that of Konrad von Gesner (1516–1565), an encyclopedic Swiss naturalist whose extensive description of animals marks the earliest beginning of modern zoology. Another eminent naturalist was Ulisse Aldrovandi (1522–1605), who founded a botanical garden at the University of Bologna and wrote voluminously on birds and insects. Still another naturalist of note was the Englishman Thomas Moufet (1553–1604), whose fine studies and drawings of insects were widely popular in his own time and after.

What lay behind the revival of anatomy? We might at first imagine that the sole cause of this renewal of interest lay in the medical profession, and it is true that the growing practice of direct dissection and more careful observation had impressed upon medical men the deficiencies of traditional anatomical knowledge. Yet of equal and in some respects greater importance was the contribution of the artists. Beginning with Giotto in the fourteenth century, artists turned to the problem of trying to depict the human figure and natural objects as they appear in nature, as they are seen in a three-dimensional space. By the end of the fifteenth century the techniques of perspective had been mastered, techniques whereby the natural world could be represented in all of its detailed variety and complexity. Artists in this period turned to the scientific study of nature out of the conviction that a true representation of things required an understanding of their inner structure and function.

We cannot underestimate the importance for the progress of biology of the development of artistic techniques during the Renaissance. All of the descriptive branches of biology rest, in the first instance, on those techniques. Even today, a good drawing is of far more use to the student of anatomy than a photograph, if only because the artist can subtly emphasize what is important in structure and function whereas the camera records everything indifferently. Nor should we assume that the progressive conquest of the artistic techniques of naturalistic representation was merely a sort of external process, as if observers really could see things the way Renaissance artists saw them and simply needed a technique to express what they saw, much as we today might buy a camera to record an object or event. On the contrary, the artists of the Renaissance *instructed* the vision of their contemporaries. As the great nineteenth-century naturalist Louis Agassiz said, "The best aid to the eye is a sharp pencil," and it is still true that the observer learns truly to see by trying to draw what he observes. The very technique by which artists represent spatial relations on a surface "informs" the observer's eye. If the mind instructs the eye, the eye in turn may instruct the mind. Until good techniques of representation were mastered, reduced to rule and generally diffused, there was no way in which an observation could be recorded so that it was available to someone else in all its accuracy and detail.

The most famous of the artist-anatomists of the Renaissance was, of course, Leonardo da Vinci (1452–1519), although his work had little influence since it was not published until the nineteenth century. He made magnificent drawings of parts of the human body, especially of the bone structures, the heart and the eye. His wide-ranging scientific interests led to remarkable studies of the flight of birds and of the structure of plants. Like other artists of the time, Leonardo undertook these scientific pursuits in the service of his artistic interests as well as for their own sake. It came to be taken for granted that an artist should study the sciences simply because he had to know the true workings of nature if he was to represent it faithfully.

The culmination of this tradition of artist-anatomist-scientist, so typical of the Italian Renaissance, was the work of the Belgian physician Andreas Vesalius (1514–1564), the greatest anatomist of modern times and the founder of modern anatomy. In 1543, the same year in which another of the greatest scientific works of modern times was published, Copernicus' treatise advancing the heliocentric theory of the solar system, Vesalius published his *De humani corporis fabrica,* "On the Structure of the Human Body." The extraordinary illustrations in this book, unprecedented in the history of anatomy and still of use to anatomists, were made by one of Titian's pupils, Jan Stevenszoon van Calcar. Like Vesalius, he had been educated in the Netherlands and had come to Italy for further study, Van Calcar to work under Titian and Vesalius to teach at the University of Padua.

Vesalius had an extraordinary gift for dissection together with a highly developed power of visualizing the structure of what he saw. Van Calcar must have possessed a similar gift of visual imagination, for it was under Vesalius' direction that he was able to draw human muscles with just the degree of contraction they have in life. The drawings in Vesalius' book are different from those in modern texts in that the artist creates for the viewer the conviction that he is looking at a living body through a transparent covering. The drawings are those of a body dynamically functional even though the studies were made on cadavers.

Vesalius' work set the study of anatomy on a new path and the medical school of Padua, already pre-eminent, achieved even greater luster. It remained the great medical school of Europe until well into the seventeenth century and drew students from all over Europe. Its most famous foreign alumnus was, of course, William Harvey. It is interesting to note that important as the work of Vesalius proved to be, he was by no means a rebel in medical matters. He had been trained at Louvain and Paris in the tradition of Galen and retained great respect for his teachings, sharing many of Galen's philosophical and theological conceptions about the perfection of the divinely made human organism. Even when Vesalius could not find any openings in the septum of the heart through which, according to Galen, the blood passed in going from one side to the other, he was most reluctant to take issue with Galen's teaching and simply reported, after considerable thought, that he could find no such openings.

Vesalius had fine students who continued his work. Perhaps the best known of these was Gabriello Fallopio (1523–1562), who made a detailed study of the reproductive system and described the tubes named after him, the Fallopian tubes, which lead from the ovaries to the uterus. Through Fallopio, the tradition of Vesalius descended to his student Geronimo Fabrizio (1537–1619). He discovered the valves in the veins and noted that they opened only in the direction of the heart and closed if the blood were forced in the opposite direction. Interestingly enough, he did not suspect from this discovery that the blood circulates in one direction, but still adhered to the Galenical theory of the ebb and flow of the blood through the veins to and from the heart. Left to find a function for these valves, he assumed that they acted to slow down but not entirely stop the ebbing movement of the Galenical venous circulation. Fabrizio was a versatile investigator, and he is considered the founder of modern embryology because of his account of the development of the chick egg, the first in modern times. Impressed by some of the important work going on in mechanics at the University of Padua, he did pioneering work in trying to interpret muscle action in mechanical terms. We might mention in passing that important work was being done in physics at this time at that same university, work which would culminate in the great contributions of Galileo, who studied and taught at Padua for a number of years.

A fellow student of Vesalius' at Paris had been the gifted Spanish physician Michael Servetus (1511–1553), who unfortunately was too fond of theological controversy for those religiously bigoted times when the republics of Holland and Venice were virtually the only tolerant states in Europe. His religious views were anathema to both Catholics and Protestants and were quite similar to the fundamental tenets of modern unitarianism. He went to Geneva to avoid the threat of Catholic persecution but fell into the hands of Calvin, who ordered him burned at the stake as a heretic. Servetus gave the first account of the pulmonary circulation, although another Paduan anatomist, Realdo Colombo (c.1516–c.1559), was working on the problem at the same time and announced his discovery somewhat later. Both of these anatomists rightly maintained that the arterial blood derives from blood which has passed through the lungs from the right ventricle of the heart. In the lungs it mingles with air before entering the left ventricle. It is important to note that neither Servetus nor Colombo was advancing a general theory of the circulation of the blood. Since no one could find any openings in the septum of the heart, anatomists looked for another mechanism by which the passage was made. Their intention was to save, not destroy, the general truth of Galen's theory of venous circulation.

The contributions of Vesalius, Fabrizio, Servetus and Colombo can all be regarded as preparations for the work of Harvey, who, as we shall see, made entirely new sense of the work of his predecessors and used the very discoveries they made to shatter the the theory of Galen. In a pattern of frequent occurrence in the history of science, Harvey did not so much discover something new as put together what was known in an entirely fresh and experimentally convincing way.

After all of this great work in anatomy had reached its peak of accomplishment, there appeared an instrument, the microscope, which was eventually to revolutionize the study of life and take men even further in their understanding of the fabric of living matter. The first recorded appearance of this instrument is 1590, when the brothers Janssen of Holland, of a family of spectacle makers, fixed two convex lenses in a tube and produced the first compound microscope.

Ancient scientists had understood something of the optical properties of curved surfaces, although spectacles were first made in Europe only at about the end of the thirteenth century, in Italy. Leonardo da Vinci had apparently made use of simple magnifying lenses to examine small objects, and contemporary with the brothers Janssen, other lens grinders and spectacle makers were contributing in theory or practice to the development of this instrument. The science of optics and glass technology were sufficiently advanced by the end of the sixteenth century for more than one person to think of combining lenses to make a compound microscope. Galileo, while designing his own telescopes, built a two-lens microscope in 1610 and observed the compound eyes of insects with it, apparently the first biological observation in microscopy. By the end of the seventeenth century, microscopes like that of Robert Hooke (1635–1703) had been developed and they were to be the high point of microscope optical design for more than one hundred years. Hooke's instrument had a condenser to concentrate light between his light source and the specimen, and the two lenses were fixed in an inclinable tube which could be focused by a screw mechanism. Although there were mechanical improvements in microscope construction after Hooke, there was no improvement in optical quality for more than one hundred years.

Along with the development of the compound microscope,

spectacle makers had improved the quality and magnifying power of single lenses, and so-called "simple" microscopes remained in use until the nineteenth century. Many of the most important early microscopists favored this instrument, for in spite of its inconvenient mechanical properties, the image it produced was in some respects superior to that of the compound microscope.

We shall have occasion to return in more detail to the optical problems of microscope design later on, when we come to discuss the great strides of nineteenth-century microscopical optics. However, we might say here that all lenses suffer from two major defects which opticians did not learn to correct until the nineteenth century and which, to that time, severely limited the capacities of the instrument. The first of these is spherical aberration, resulting from the fact that the light passing through a lens cannot all be brought to a common focus because of the very curvature of the lens itself. The light passing through the central region will focus further along the optical axis than that passing through the regions of the lens closer to the rim. In practice this means that an object in focus at the center of the viewer's field will be out of focus in the rest of the field. The greater the curvature of the lens, the greater the magnification, so that the more powerful the lens the more noticeable the spherical aberration will be.

Another defect is called chromatic aberration. This means that any lens acts to some degree like a prism and breaks up white light into its component colors. Since these are of different wavelengths, they will come to a focus at different points along the optical axis. The observer detects this aberration as a rainbowlike halo surrounding the specimen and its structures. As with spherical aberration, chromatic aberration becomes more marked the greater the magnification and curvature of the lens.

In the early compound microscopes such defects were even more severe than in the simple microscopes of the same magnifying power. The ocular lens of the two-lens microscopes not only magnified the image of the objective lens but also magnified the defects of that image. The resultant image was therefore inferior to that of a simple lens. The image of the latter would be blurred at the edges, but at the center it would be sharper than anything the compound microscope could render. Since the simple lens of high magnification had to be quite small, very curved and held quite close to the eye, there was considerable convenience in using the compound microscope and it was certainly adequate for many purposes. Still, it is no accident that the most remarkable microscopist of the seventeenth century, Anton van Leeuwenhoek (1632–1723), used a simple microscope. Besides the advantages already mentioned, Leeuwenhoek seems to have realized that the small lenses required for a simple microscope could be made of optically homogeneous pieces of glass. It is surprising to realize that glass technology had not yet been able to produce even fairly large pieces of glass free from defects and inclusions.

Among the greatest of the seventeenth-century microscopists was Jan Swammerdam (1637–1680), a Dutchman tragically marked by severe mental illness who nevertheless was one of the greatest observers in the history of biology. His dissections of minute insects were so exact that it is hard to believe they were done with such simple and crude instruments as he possessed. He was the first to detect corpuscles in blood and to observe the cleavages in frogs' eggs. His work remained without much influence, unfortunately, since the bulk of it was not published until long after his death.

Another Dutch microscopist, Regnier de Graaf (1641–1673), studied the fine structures of the mammalian reproductive system and discovered the structure still called after him, the Graafian follicle. He mistook the follicle, however, for the mammalian egg itself, an error which continued in general circulation until the nineteenth century. In Italy, Malpighi discovered the capillaries in the lungs of a frog (1661) and completed the theory of the circulation of the blood three years after the death of Harvey. In England, the botanist Nehemiah Grew (1641–1712) made detailed studies of the structure of plants and flowers, examining plant tissues in thin sections and making careful descriptions of the different kinds of pollen grains. Also in England, Robert Hooke, who made contributions to other branches of science, was an enthusiastic microscopist. His *Micrographia* (1665), like the books of other microscopists of the time, is beautifully illustrated. To him we owe the word "cell," from the Latin for room. Observing a thin slice of cork, Hooke noted the small empty rectangles which made up its structure and suggested that they resembled small rooms.

The prince of seventeenth-century microscopists, however, was Leeuwenhoek. By profession a draper, he spent all of his spare time making his own microscopes and looking at just about everything he could get his hands on. He became so skilled that he was able to make minute lenses giving as much as two hundred diameters of useful magnification. These were scarcely larger than the head of a pin, and the plate in which they were mounted would have had to be held so close to the eye that we can only wonder at the patience and discipline of this remarkable man, perhaps the greatest and most energetic amateur in the history of science.

Leeuwenhoek made extended observations of blood corpuscles and of the capillaries as well as other tissues, carrying further the work of Swammerdam and Malpighi, and looked at many of the favorite objects of the microscopists of his time,—the wings of flies, the larvae of oysters, the scales of a fish and the like. His greatest observations, however, concerned his discovery of the "marvelous animals" which we today know as the protozoa. His descriptions of the organisms he saw are so accurate that we can identify them today. It also seems certain that he was the first to observe bacteria, although even the larger bacteria are not easily seen at the magnifications he worked with. Without realizing it, he also discovered the first pathogenic microorganism when he detected a small protozoan, *Giardia intestinalis,* in his stool when he was sick with diarrhea. Together with an assistant he first observed spermatozoa and opened up, as we shall see, a whole new phase in the controversies over the nature of fertilization and the problem of preformation. The many remarkable observations of Leeuwenhoek were recounted in a series of letters to the Royal Society in

England, and they are fascinating reading. The freshness and excitement of his discoveries still shine through his account.

Of all the fields of biological inquiry, two are more completely dependent on the microscope than perhaps any others: cytology and microbiology. Leeuwenhoek is unquestionably the founder of microbiology. More than any other of the early microscopists, he opened up a whole new biological dimension and raised new problems for biologists as well as new versions of some of the old problems. His discovery of the protozoa gave a new twist to the age-old question of spontaneous generation. Francesco Redi (1626–1697), a Florentine physician and naturalist, had shown in a number of elegantly designed experiments (1668) that maggots would not be produced in decaying meat if flies were prevented from laying eggs on it by a gauze covering over the vessel containing the meat. From ancient times maggots had been among the favorite organisms for the adherents of spontaneous generation to point to, and Redi had now proved that they come from eggs. His experiments were quite convincing to a large number of other investigators, and it did seem as if the larger organisms, at least, could not come into being through spontaneous generation. But what of these tiny organisms that Leeuwenhoek had discovered? Might not such apparently simple creatures arise directly out of nonliving matter? As we shall see, it took a long time to settle this question.

Leeuwenhoek's observation of spermatozoa gave a new direction to the debate between the proponents of epigenesis in development and the preformationists. Some microscopists thought they saw a complete miniature individual in the head of the spermatozoon and felt they had visible proof of preformation. Others, also preformationists, denied seeing any such creature and left preformation to the female. We shall later consider this curious chapter in the history of biology when "spermists" and "ovists" hotly debated whether the preformed individual came from the father or the mother.

After the brilliant achievements of the seventeenth century, microscopy languished in the eighteenth. New species of protozoa were discovered, the beginnings of classification of bacteria were made, and extended observations were made on plant and animal tissues, but no contribution of the first importance was made through the use of the microscope during this century. Part of the reason for this doubtless lay in the fact that glass technology and optics had not progressed far enough to contribute to the substantial improvement of the microscope. Even such ordinary accessories as glass slides and cover slips were not produced until the nineteenth century, not to mention improved lenses.

It would nevertheless be misleading to say that if better microscopes had been available, ample use would have been made of them. Biology itself had to advance to a new point at which investigators would find an improved microscope useful. For example, until substantial progress had been made in anatomy, as it was in the sixteenth century, there would have been little point in trying to study the fine structure of tissues and organs. It was precisely the rapid growth of knowledge of gross anatomy and physiology that had drawn the attention of investigators to the finer detail which could not be seen by the naked eye. Vesalius and his successors therefore were the indispensable prerequisite for the work of a Malpighi, for example. It is also true, however, that the great seventeenth-century microscopists were, for the most part, loners. They founded no school, left no disciples, and the greatest of them all, Leeuwenhoek, was an amateur with no academic standing whatever. In spite of all the microscopical activity of the seventeenth century, microscopy did not become part of any formal system of instruction until the nineteenth.

The work of the Renaissance naturalists, the voyages of discovery, the revelations of the microscope, had opened men's eyes, to a hitherto unparalleled extent, to the diversity of life. Antiquity had bequeathed descriptions of only about five hundred animals and not many more plants. In the space of two hundred years, from about 1500 to 1700, literally thousands of new organisms had been added to the inventory of living things. In the light of this fact, the eighteenth-century biologists were almost predestined to undertake the task of systematic description and classification of these newly discovered organisms, and much of the achievement of eighteenth-century biology lies in this field.

The task of classification is not as simple as it might appear. We have seen that Aristotle worked out important taxonomic concepts such as those of species and genus, and applied these concepts to a limited number of organisms. Eighteenth-century biologists had many more and more varied organisms to classify, so that some of the problems Aristotle disposed of easily were very present to them. For example, the far greater variety of organisms they were acquainted with made the whole task of defining species a more difficult one. It is not easy to say in every instance what constitutes a species, especially if you assume, as everyone did until the nineteenth century, that species are fixed and immutable. Today we know that species are in continual change and that there is a spectrum of variation within an interbreeding population. Indeed, the old concept of species has changed from a concept of fixed "type" to that of an interbreeding population in a state of dynamic equilibrium. Moreover, we can only define a species in terms of one phase, however long, in the evolutionary history of a given population of interbreeding organisms.

In any case, the requirement for a system of biological classification is not to find a place for everything, so to speak, as if one had a filing cabinet to fill up, but to find a place for everything *which makes biological sense*. As Aristotle realized, one cannot use a single dichotomous system to classify organisms without getting into trouble. In practice, therefore, taxonomists and systematists use a variety of principles in arranging living things. In botany, the leaf and the structure of the reproductive organs are crucial criteria. In zoology, as Aristotle grasped, the body plan is of determinative importance.

The foundations for the great development of systematics in the eighteenth century began to be laid in the seventeenth. The work of John Ray (1627–1705) was the first truly major contribution to taxonomy in modern times. He not only described thousands of varieties of plants and animals, he also tried to find fresh and useful criteria for classifying them. For example, he divided all mammals into those with toes or those with hoofs. The latter were in turn subdivided into three groups according to the structure of the hoof. Further subdivisions introduced new criteria such as whether or not a particular category of hoofed animal chewed the cud or not, whether it possessed horns and, if it did, whether those horns were permanent or shed and regrown annually.

Although Ray's system is obsolete we can detect in it the thinking of a truly gifted taxonomist. Whether an animal has toes or hoofs, whether it chews the cud or not, such categories are biologically sound in that they point to quite different ways of living and significantly different anatomical structures.

The greatest taxonomist of modern times was undoubtedly Carl von Linné (1707–1778), a native of Sweden, who is better known under his latinized name of Linnaeus. His great work was the *Systema naturae* (1735), a complete arrangement of all the known species. Although in some fundamental respects his system of classification was not as good as Aristotle's, he has the merit of carrying the process of subdivision to a high degree of intelligent refinement. Moreover, he introduced the systematic practice of binomial nomenclature, that is, of giving each organism a double name, one indicating the genus and the other the species.

With such a system every organism can be adequately named in such a way that its relationship to its nearest of kind is indicated. The universal adoption of this practice and of Latin nomenclature has given biologists in all countries of the world a common terminology. Linnaeus is also remembered as the scientist who gave mankind its scientific name, *Homo sapiens,*— literally, "rational man," although one is tempted to think that this name applies to mankind less often than it might.

Systems of classification have varied pretty much in the past —and they still do in details—but we have now settled on the following general categories descending from the most inclusive to the least: Kingdom, Phylum, Class, Order, Family, Genus and Species. There are further subgroupings of these, such as subphylum or subclass, but in general outline the scheme for man would run as follows: Kingdom, Animalia; Phylum, Chordata; Class, Mammalia; Order, Primata; Family, Hominidae; Genus, Homo; Species, *Homo sapiens.*

Taxonomy is not a static part of biological science, although it might seem so at first glance. Each advance in biological knowledge affects it; our present system of classification reflects as much as we have been able to learn of the evolutionary history of life, and our growing knowledge of genetics may change it even further. As Aristotle himself realized, no system of classification will do complete justice to all the variety of life and the often minute gradations to be found in that variety. It is, nevertheless, an indispensable part of the process of knowledge that we impose general principles of order on all of the bits and pieces of data that we have been able to gather, however much some of these data may escape our tidy categories.

All taxonomic systems, since the time of Aristotle, are arranged as a hierarchy of simple to complex, and to some degree, life can be intelligently ordered as such. Both for Aristotle and for most of his successors down to modern times, this hierarchy or ladder was not only fixed but was in one way or another thought to be a ladder of values. Each species, in this view, represented some metaphysical "type" or "idea," and the hierarchy of taxonomy was thought to be the very order of nature itself. Notions like "lower" and "higher" forms of life, and "simple" and "complex," tended to become equated with degrees of perfection or "nobility." More than one systematist, under religious or philosophical influences, was inclined to see all of life as a pyramid of fixed types, each higher than the other, all created by God to sustain man, the noblest of creatures, at the apex.

We have rejected the notion of species as eternal types, and have come to think of them as populations in which variation is normal and not merely a deviation from the type. We have also rejected the notion of hierarchy as anything more than a metaphor for certain kinds of relationships which obtain between living things. Some of the most enthusiastic proponents of evolution at one time were sufficiently under the influence of older modes of thought to conceive of the taxonomic hierarchy as a sort of map of evolution itself, leading step by step to man as the pinnacle of nature. Modern biology has nothing to say about such anthropocentric assumptions. Such or similar ideas are not within the realm of questions that science can or should try to answer. So today evolutionists prefer to talk of the radiation of phyla, the "spreading out" of life, rather than use the misleading rhetoric of life's slow climb out of primeval ooze.

iii *The Physics and Chemistry of Life*

The great discoveries of Galileo Galilei (1564–1642), his creation of modern mathematical physics, his brilliant contributions to mechanics, changed the general conception of what the model of a true science should be. So illuminating were his results, so lucid his methods, that he turned mathematical physics into the very ideal of scientific knowledge. All of nature was like a book written in mathematical language, the language and weighing and measuring, and all phenomena were really to be explained in terms of their quantitative aspects. René Descartes (1596–1650), the great French philosopher and mathematician, was profoundly impressed by the work of Galileo, and he had himself placed a powerful new instrument in the hands of scientists with his invention of analytical geometry. After what had seemed like so many centuries of scientific stagnation, spectacular new knowledge, at least in physics, mathematics and astronomy, had come to light, and in these fields modern man had advanced well beyond the ancients.* Descartes

* Both Descartes and Francis Bacon (1561–1626) exerted great influence on the mode in which scientific research was organized in the

raised the question as to whether or not these new methods of inquiry might be applied to biological phenomena. He systematically expounded the concept of the living organism as a machine entirely explicable in terms of the new concepts of mechanics. He saw no reason why the body should not be studied by exactly the same methods physicists applied to levers, pulleys, pendulums and pumps.

Descartes reserved for man an immaterial immortal soul, but his body and the bodies of all the lower animals (who had no souls) were to be understood as mechanisms. Harvey had himself shown that the heart behaved like a "water bellows" and that its bicuspid valves were like the valves, or "clacks," as he called them, which operate in a pump. Harvey was no Cartesian, but his proof for the circulation of the blood was a model of physical and mechanistic reasoning and was most welcome to the biological mechanists. With Descartes there began, in its most significant form, the long debate in the history of biology between mechanists and vitalists. The mechanists proposed that living systems could be understood in terms of the same principles which govern inanimate nature. The heart is a pump, bones are levers, the stomach is a meat grinder, the lungs are bellows. The vitalists, on the other hand, proposed that all living systems are fundamentally different from nonliving things. Living creatures are intelligible only in relation to laws or principles which are manifest exclusively in them. You cannot understand organisms entirely in terms of their physical and chemical constituents.

In the course of time, the mechanistic view came to be called "reductionistic" in that the mechanists purported to explain the properties of living things by reducing them to the properties of nonliving things. Their hope was that complex biological phe-

---

seventeenth century. The growth of scientific academies, so characteristic of the modern world of science, stems in part from the conviction of these two influential thinkers that the progress of science would involve the organization of cooperative societies which would pool the specialized contributions of their members. On this development, see my *Renaissance and Revolution* (New York, 1965), the chapter on Bacon and the new philosophy.

nomena would turn out to be patterns of simpler, "inanimate" chemical and physicochemical processes. In short, in their view, biological laws would eventually be expounded in terms of laws ascertained in other branches of science, namely physics and chemistry. The vitalists claimed that this would prove to be impossible.

Mechanism or reductionism of one kind or another has turned out to be a far more fruitful hypothesis in the history of biology than vitalism. The Italian physiologist Giovanni Alfonso Borelli (1608–1679), applying Cartesian ideas, gave a brilliant interpretation of muscular and bone action in terms of mechanical principles, especially the principle of "contraction," although he was less successful in trying to explain digestion as the result of purely mechanical stomach action in grinding up food, or the action of the lungs as that of a simple mechanical air pump. His work was nevertheless successful enough to give a great impetus to mechanistic interpretations of physiological processes.

Vitalism, on the whole, has been sterile in the history of biology, even though some great biologists were convinced vitalists. To do justice to both sides we must distinguish between intelligent and simple-minded versions of both these positions. First of all, mechanism and reductionism take different forms according to the state of physics and chemistry. The simple lever-pulley machine that Descartes had in mind could explain to a great degree the operations of bones and muscles. However, the Cartesian mechanistic model broke down when it was applied to the digestive or respiratory system; it simply could not describe what these systems in fact do. And such a model is far too simple to even begin to explain behavior. The invention of computers in our own times has revived machine analogies for behavior, but a computer is a far more complex machine than anything the Cartesians ever envisaged. It can handle symbols in systematic ways and it has complex feedback mechanisms which permit it to vary its workings in ways that resemble variations in behavior. Nevertheless, with all its great utility, even this new analogy breaks down at some points in its application to the behavior of living things. Those vitalists who opposed Cartesian principles in biology did in fact point to the very real inadequacies of mechanistic explanation. Yet they did not grasp how much could be learned if organisms were approached *as if* they were machines, nor how useless it is to appeal to obscure metaphysical or spiritual principles which lie beyond any scientific analysis or verification.

Along with reduction to mechanical principles, the seventeenth century saw the introduction of chemical reductionism in biology, although the chemistry of the time was far too primitive to permit of any real progress in this direction. The Renaissance Swiss alchemist Paracelsus (1493?–1541) had introduced the use of chemical therapeutics into medicine on the ground that the body itself was a kind of chemical system and that chemical drugs would therefore be effective where the botanical drugs of tradition were not. He did in fact cure syphilis with mercurials, when his doses were not so drastic that they did harm to the patient. A Flemish disciple of Paracelsus, the alchemist Jan Baptista van Helmont (1577–1644), tried the first chemical experiment on a living organism that we know about. He grew a willow tree, which he had weighed, in a weighed amount of soil for five years, adding only water. At the end of this time he found that the tree had gained 164 pounds and that the soil had lost only two ounces. He concluded that the tree derived its substance from the water and not from the soil. He was, as we know now, quite right about the soil but wrong about the water. Although one of the earliest experimenters with gases (he coined the word "gas"), he did not reckon that the plant might derive its substance from the surrounding atmosphere. Oddly enough, he even discovered the source of the plant's substance, carbon dioxide—which he called *spiritus sylvestris,* or spirit of the wood—without guessing that it might be the agent he was looking for in his experiment with the willow.

Another seventeenth-century medical alchemist, Franz de la Boë, known as Franciscus Sylvius (1614–1672) from the Latin version of his name, proposed that the body was a chemical system and endeavored to give a consistent account of body functioning in such terms. He was much less given to mystical ideas than either Paracelsus or Van Helmont and spent a good deal of his time working on salts. He was among the first to clearly grasp that salts were produced by reactions between acids and alkalis, and worked out a theory of physiological functions in chemical terms. Acidity, alkalinity and fermentation were the three fundamental chemical processes which accounted for all vital activity in sickness or health. He was, moreover, quite explicit that fermentation was a purely chemical process and that it was, in principle, identical with the process of digestion. This chemical conception of digestion came to be pitted against the strictly mechanical theory proposed by Borelli and the question was not decided, as we shall see, until the classic experiments of Réaumur in the eighteenth century. Before either of these theories was advanced, people generally accepted the ancient explanation of digestion as a kind of "boiling," however little that actually explained anything.

It is clear that these attempts at chemical reductionism, even when they were closer to the truth than their alternatives, were too obscure to be of very much use. Neither the chemistry of fermentation nor that of digestion was understood, given the state of chemical knowledge of the time, in detailed and explicit terms. Chemical understanding of vital processes had really to await the great work of Lavoisier and Priestley in the eighteenth century to find a fruitful start.

It should be clear, from these examples, that the power of a chemical or physical concept to explain a biological process depends to a very high degree on the level of sophistication and richness of the concept, how it is applied, and what specific biological data one wishes to interpret by its means. As new concepts arise in physics and chemistry they often enough find their application in biology and sometimes in erroneous but fruitful ways. When Luigi Galvani (1737–1798) accidentally discovered in 1786 that the legs of a dead frog twitched when an electrical current passed through them, he initiated the attempt to use concepts from electromagnetic phenomena to interpret living things in addition to or instead of concepts from mechanics and chemistry. If Descartes wanted to reduce the body to machines made of levers, pulleys and the like, Galvani thought it might be reduced to an electrical machine and advanced influential if erroneous notions concerning "animal electricity." Nevertheless, his work is a good example of some of the ironies of scientific advance. In this case a good observation led to an erroneous but very fruitful conclusion. In fact Galvani did not know that he had generated an electrical current. His frog's leg was attached to a brass hook and when the leg came in contact with a silver plate the leg twitched. Later on Alessandro Volta (1745–1827) showed that Galvani had, in fact, accidentally made a kind of battery. Galvani's conclusion was that the animal itself generated electricity. In fact animals do, although he picked the wrong example. Nevertheless, there is a direct line from the work of Galvani to that of the German physiologist Emil du Bois-Reymond (1818–1896), who demonstrated the fact that a nervous impulse is always accompanied by a change in electrical charge along the nerve.

With Galvani, a new kind of physical reductionism entered the arena of biological thought and more sophisticated possibilities of physical explanation became possible. Albrecht von Haller, a remarkable and versatile Swiss polymath (1708–1777), put physiology on the path toward modernity with his theory of the irritability of protoplasm. In his view it was an intrinsic property of protoplasm to respond to stimuli whether from external sources directly or through the medium of nerve stimuli. This was the thesis of his book *Elementa physiologiae corporis humani* (1759–1766), which remained a standard text for many years.

In the nineteenth century, further application of physical principles to phenomena of the nervous system came with the work of Johannes Müller (1801–1858), who, along with the Frenchman Claude Bernard and the German Du Bois-Reymond, was among the greatest physiologists of the century. Müller formulated the principle of "specific nerve energies," which means that the kind of sensation we receive depends not on the mode of stimulation of the nerve but on the characteristics of the sense organ with which the nerve is linked. Thus mechanical stimulation of the optic nerve will produce light sensations and no other. That is why a man who is struck on the head may "see stars." Müller's *Handbook of Human Physiology* (1833–1840) became the great physiology text of his time, as Von Haller's had been in the eighteenth century.

Claude Bernard (1813–1878) was not only a brilliant experimenter and investigator but also a profound thinker who was able to generalize his specific data into principles of great importance. Two of his greatest contributions to physiology concerned the function of the liver and of the pancreas. He discovered that the liver is a chemical factory, so to speak. It takes from the nutrients brought to it by the blood, substances which it modifies and stores against the future energy needs of the body. The most important of these storage products is glycogen, "animal starch," made up of many molecules of the sugar glucose arranged in long chains of "polysaccharides," from the Greek for "many sugars." As the body requires energy, the glycogen is broken down and released to the body according to the specific needs. What Bernard showed of momentous significance for physiology was that the body can build up as well as break down chemical substances and that, moreover, it performs these functions according to the particular requirements of the organism at a certain time.

Bernard also demonstrated that digestion is not completed in the stomach, but that after food enters the intestine, the pancreatic juices flowing into it play a crucial role in the metabolism of fats. Another great discovery of Bernard's concerned the circulatory system. Muscle fibers had been discovered surrounding the walls of the smaller arteries, and Bernard showed that the expansion and contraction of these muscles controls the supply of blood to the tissues. Moreover, he traced the activity of the muscles to a complex nerve system.

Now these discoveries, important in themselves, suggested to Bernard certain principles of the first importance. As he put it, "All vital mechanisms, different as they may be from one another, have only one purpose, that of maintaining in a constant state the conditions of life in the internal environment." There is a constant *milieu intérieur*, an internal environment, in all living things, and the organism preserves it despite external changes. Indeed, the organs of the body are not more or less independent of one another but are continually interacting in their functions. They interact in a dynamic equilibrium, a homeostatic balance. The body regulates its temperature, its storage or consumption of energy-producing substances, its distribution of bodily fluids, all in answer to physiological needs of the organism as a whole and in the interest of maintaining a constant internal state. If an organism depends in some obvious sense on its environment, it must also compensate for changes in that environment if it is to survive.

The progress of physiology since Bernard's time has served to show how sensitive and complex the interior environment really is. The immunological response of the body, the way it develops antibodies of extreme specificity against invading microorganisms or foreign substances, is a remarkable example of the extraordinary compensatory capacities of the living organism.

If mechanism of one kind or another was the fruitful course for biology, some mechanists were not above being simple-minded about it. Descartes himself drew some astonishing conclusions from his kind of reductionism when he insisted that suffering animals, no matter how much they howled or writhed, felt no pain. How could they, if they were machines? The result of this belief was that some Cartesians in the seventeenth century and after performed experiments of astonishing cruelty on animals in the secure belief that the animals felt no pain, no matter how much they seemed to! A more recent, if less cruel, example of simple-minded reductionism can be found in the Sunday-supplement articles which were popular not long ago, soberly contending that the human body is really nothing more than a couple of dollars worth of chemical elements.

Simple-minded vitalism had, however, the defect of explaining nothing at all, even though not all forms of vitalism were simple-minded. In fact the vitalists, at times, had the merit of calling attention to the inadequacy of the physics and chemistry of the time in affording thorough explanations of biological phenomena. The reply of the mechanists, and it was a fruitful one, was to wait on the progress of physics and chemistry.

From our contemporary point of view this historically important controversy has lost much meaning. For one thing, biologists are by no means confined to only one kind of explanation, or to a choice between mechanism and vitalism. Evolutionary biology, ecology and other branches of biology use principles, like adaptation or the reciprocity of structure and function, which are in themselves neither mechanistic nor vitalistic. Moreover, as more than one thinker in modern times has pointed out, living matter displays properties which are not found as such in its constituents and which are proper only to matter organized in that particular way. This no more constitutes vitalism than pointing out that water is quite different in its physical and chemical properties from either the hydrogen or the oxygen that are its constituents. The organization of living things is enormously complex, but a fuller understanding of it may reveal new chemical and physical laws which are peculiar to that level of organization. When we discover them we may simply have to change our minds about what should be included under physics and chemistry.

What Galileo was to physics and astronomy, William Harvey (1578–1657) was to experimental physiology. Although he was no Cartesian and no physicist, his work was a triumph of the application of exact quantitative methods to a biological problem of the first importance. It became for years the model of what the "new philosophy," as science was then called, might accomplish in the understanding of life.

Before we can consider the greatness of Harvey's work we shall have to glance at the physiological theories of Galen, whose conception of the circulation of the blood remained the prevailing one in spite of threats from the discourses of the great Paduan anatomists. Galen hypothesized that the heart was a heat-producing "chemical" organ and that the fundamental "chemical" materials of life were certain spirits which were found in or arose from the blood. The liver continually generated fresh blood, eventually used up in the tissues, and filled it with "natural spirit," required for the performance of the simplest activities of living things. Veins took this blood from the liver to the right ventricle of the heart, and this venous blood ebbed and flowed from liver to heart and back again. This was in fact the essential circulation of the blood. At first, Greek anatomists had thought that the arteries carried only air; since they are empty in corpses, the anatomists assumed they were also empty in life. In fact the word "artery" means air duct. By Galen's time, however, it was well established that some blood did enter the arteries. This was thought to be a small amount, and Galen believed that it passed through tiny, invisible pores in the septum of the heart from the right ventricle to the left. There the blood met air brought directly to the left ventricle from the lungs and was turned into "vital spirit." The greater amount of venous blood simply left its impurities in the right ventricle of the heart, where they were passed on to the lungs for elimination, and flowed back to the liver. The arteries, on the other hand, distributed the vital spirit to different parts of the body, where it made possible higher biological functions such as the sensory ones. Some of the vital spirit went to the brain, where it was changed into "animal spirit" ("animal" here meaning "soul-like," from the Latin *anima*, soul); this spirit was required for the higher and more intellectual activities. It is clear from this account that the blood did not in fact circulate, that it simply ebbed and flowed through the venous system. A small amount, vital spirit, was distributed through the arteries. The animal spirit formed in the brain was carried elsewhere through the nerves, which were thought to be hollow. What we have here is really three different systems of making and distributing three different substances, an elaboration of the three-vessel physiology of Erasistratus which we considered earlier.

As we have seen, certain discoveries had shaken this ancient conception of the circulation of the blood. Vesalius had not found the invisible pores in the septum, Fabrizio had discovered the valves of the veins, while Servetus and Colombo had tried to salvage Galen with their discovery of the pulmonary circulation. Vesalius reluctantly admitted, after twenty years, that there simply were no pores in the septum and Fabrizio, to please the shade of Galen, decided that the valves really could not block the presumed reverse flow of blood in the veins. In short, these discoverers either admitted ignorance of how Galen's theory might be made to work or interpreted their own discoveries to fit the older theory. We need not assume because of this that they were especially benighted or timid. No scientist, even today, is eager to scrap a plausible theory in the absence of any cogent alternative, and often enough a theory is patched up and modified many times before it is finally set aside for another one.

This, in any case, was the situation when Harvey began his work on the circulation of the blood. He studied the circulatory systems in a wide variety of animals, and in a number of simple experiments showed, in the first instance, that the valves in both veins and arteries were one-way valves. They seemed to direct the blood, not to block it. (The valves in the arteries had been observed by Galen and rediscovered by Leonardo.) Working with snakes, which were quite suitable for these experiments since the hearts of cold-blooded animals beat more slowly than those of mammals, Harvey showed that if he tied off an artery, the side of the vessel nearer the heart would bulge, and that if he tied off a vein, the side away from the heart would bulge. This demonstrated that there was no reversal of the blood flow in the veins or arteries. The heart, moreover, was clearly a muscle, for it became harder when contracted, with just the same kind of tension one might feel in the muscle of the flexed arm. It was also clear that the contraction of the heart coincided with the expansion of the arteries. The pulse or expansion of the arteries was not the result of arterial action, as others had thought, but was the work of the heart pushing blood into them. Harvey confirmed this by noting that the spurting of blood from a severed artery coincided with ventricular contraction.

In a further series of experiments, Harvey showed that the

auricles or atria of the heart have a relation to the ventricles analogous to that of ventricles to the arteries: that is, the auricles rhythmically pump blood into the ventricles. This fact was determined by noting the correlation between the auricular contraction and the spurting of blood from a cut ventricle. Harvey also observed that, since the contraction of the ventricle follows that of the auricle, the same blood which is pumped by the auricle into the ventricle is pumped by the latter into the artery.

Some of these observations had been made before Harvey, and it is perfectly clear that Harvey was influenced by the work of his teacher Fabrizio and others. The mark of his genius was to bring all of the material of his predecessors into a new relation with his own remarkable observations. At no point is this genius more evident than in his famous "calculus." In his analysis of the one-directional flow of blood through the cardiac valves, Harvey points out that the blood not only circulates in one direction but that this circulation is uninterrupted. Let us, he suggests, reflect on the size of the heart and its chambers. The ventricle of the heart of a man will hold about two ounces of blood. The normal pulse is about seventy-two beats a minute. Each beat will throw two ounces of blood into the aorta. In one hour the left ventricle will pump 8,640 ounces of blood into the aorta, an amount of blood which is three times the weight of a well-built man of 180 pounds! Where can all of this blood have come from? Where can it all go to? To deny that the blood circulates is to be forced into an absurdity.

The force of this argument was astonishingly compelling; nothing like it exists in biological literature before that time. It had the kind of logical rigor which had hitherto marked the work of physicists like Galileo. Moreover, it had this logical rigor in spite of the fact that Harvey had no direct evidence of how the blood got from the arteries to the veins. There had to be some connection even if it was not observable. Harvey did not assume that the connections had to be enclosed. That is, he left open the question as to whether or not the blood is retained in minute vessels—the capillaries later discovered by Malpighi

—or whether it is poured into porous tissues at the fine ends of the arteries and reintroduced into the circulatory system at the fine ends of the veins. We might point out that Harvey might not have found the discovery of capillaries—had he lived to see them—a discovery without problems for him. He knew that the blood carried nutrients, and in the light of the fact that nothing was known about permeable membranes and osmosis at that time, the notion that the blood was poured directly into the tissues at the fine ends of the arterial system would at least have explained how body tissues received their nourishment. In other words, however compelling the circulation argument was, a completely self-enclosed circulatory system would have had, for Harvey, no physiological function.

If Galen had to posit invisible pores in the septum, Harvey too had to posit invisible connections between veins and arteries, whether vessels, or pores and cavities in the tissues. This fact does not make their theories intellectual equivalents. Harvey was essentially correct and Galen was not. Harvey's observations and his "calculus" made any other conclusion than the one he came to absurd *in spite of* the fact that he could not explain every difficulty. Harvey's work is thus the real beginning of experimental physiology, for he was the first to apply mathematical and quantitative reasoning to the solution of a biological problem. His conclusions were based not simply on observation, important as that was, but on the correlation of his observations with one another and on rigorous deduction from the assembled evidence. His method, in some essentials, resembles the brilliant deductions of physical phenomena from mathematical formulations of observations so typical of Galileo's procedures.

Although Harvey had enormous respect for Galen and for Aristotle—he even attributed the discovery of pulmonary circulation erroneously to Galen on the basis of some obscure passages—his contribution initiated the process of undermining Galen's physiology for good and all. The whole theory of "spirits" was doomed to fall when Harvey explained that the arteries are full of blood in life and are empty in corpses only because the cessation of heart action occurs after the cessation of respiration, so that the blood is pushed into the veins by the heart action but no fresh blood enters the arteries through the heart from the lungs. His discovery, like so many others, created opposition in medical circles, but gradually came to be accepted. Part of the opposition came from the fact that Harvey demanded of his readers the capacity to understand a logically rigorous argument from clear evidence, but from evidence which was in some respects incomplete. His readers had to understand that something must be so even if he could not show the precise way in which it was so in every respect. Indeed, some of his critics pointed out that the connections between veins and arteries were just as invisible as the pores Galen assumed existed in the septum. This controversy illustrates one important thing about scientific work: it is a way of thinking about evidence as much as a way of getting data. In effect, Harvey posited the existence of a structure of some kind connecting veins and arteries without being at all certain what that structure might be like. Something like this has happened over and over again in the history of science. After all, our first conceptions of atoms and genes were demanded more by logical necessity than by direct evidence.

Harvey was also influenced in his views by ideas which we might consider archaic, such as the notion derived from his beloved Aristotle that circular motion was more perfect than other kinds of motion, and the ancient conception of the blood as the noblest of bodily fluids. In fact, he felt that a perfect circular motion was somehow more appropriate to this noblest of fluids than any other kind. Such notions are utterly foreign to modern science, but more than once in the history of science an investigator has felt his way about in the unknown with the aid of analogues we would find odd as well as with precise observations and accurate measurements.

Whatever Harvey's philosophical views may have been, his work represented the fusion of the great Paduan tradition of meticulous anatomical and physiological study with the experimental methods so dear to the followers of Francis Bacon, and the mathematical methods of the proponents of the mechanical philosophy of Descartes. Harvey was by no means a Cartesian, nor did he think much of what Bacon had to say about science and scientific method. Nevertheless, his work served to strengthen the prestige of mechanistic currents in biological thought.

Harvey was also interested in embryology, and in an age when facile explanations of naive preformationism were widely diffused he adhered strictly to the epigenetic theories of his master Aristotle. It was part of Harvey's genius not to explain more than he could account for, and his careful observations of embryonic development in chicks left no room for fanciful conjectures about preformation. He was the first to note that the part of the hen's egg which develops into the chick is what is now called the blastoderm, not, as other observers thought, the chalazae, the very conspicuous spirals of albumen which connect the egg to its membrane, and which you can see for yourself the next time you open an egg.

Harvey would have to be called an ovist, although he was not a preformationist. *Ex ovo omnia,* "all organisms rise from the egg," he firmly maintained, although what he may have thought the mammalian egg to be like is necessarily obscure, since no one had ever seen one. In this he probably adhered to the general explanation to be found in Aristotle, that the homologue of the avian or reptilian egg was the stage of the mammalian embryo in which it is surrounded by a membrane. Harvey's view of the role of semen in fertilization was also derived from the Aristotelian tradition. An *aura seminalis,* a power inherent in the semen, initiated development. The egg acted as matter to the form- and structure-giving power of the seminal fluid. Harvey thus rejected the ancient view of the atomists that both the father and mother contributed matter to the embryo in fertilization. He did so not only because that view was associated with doctrines of preformation—Epicurus had argued that the parental mixture of atoms was a preformed miniature embryo—but because Harvey was a vitalist in the same sense that Aristotle was. Living matter manifested principles of organization and function which could not be described in terms of the random process of atomistic materialism.

We have already pointed out that the discovery of microscopic forms of life had given a new force to the old theory of "abiogenesis," of the spontaneous generation of life out of nonliving matter. Aristotle had believed in the spontaneous generation of both plants and the lower animals, but in the course of time the number of candidates for this phenomenon had been reduced to only the smallest forms of life. It is an interesting irony in the history of biology that those who argued for spontaneous generation should have been in principle closer to reductionist or mechanistic concepts of life than the vitalists. The latter, at least if they were pretty consistent in their views, would have to deny that anything living could arise from nonliving matter. It took a long time for many biologists to be convinced that, at least under present conditions there is only biogenesis: Living things originate only from other living things. Yet those who argued for spontaneous generation were in a sense advocating the idea that some forms of life at least could be explained in terms of physicochemical principles and that there was no unbridgeable gulf between that which is alive and that which is not. In a vastly different context we would agree with this last proposition, yet in retrospect, the "right" side in the seventeenth century would have been with those who denied the possibility of spontaneous generation. Like preformation, the theory of spontaneous generation had a truth buried in it, but it was to take much more knowledge and effort before that truth could be extracted.

As we have seen, Redi had settled the question of spontaneous generation for maggots and, by implication, for a lot of other creatures of small size. It was not until the following century that a brilliant Italian scientist, Lazzaro Spallanzani, attempted to decide the problem for microorganisms. He showed that if a nutrient broth was sufficiently heated before it was sealed and the seal made tight enough, no microorganisms would develop in it. His experiments answered the claim of the

English investigator John Turberville Needham (1731–1781) to have generated microscopic forms of life spontaneously under similar conditions. Spallanzani was simply a more careful and meticulous experimenter than Needham and showed that Needham's results were due to incomplete sterilization and faulty sealing of the vessels containing the nutrient broth. We shall have occasion to return to Spallanzani, who was the greatest experimental biologist of his time and the true father of modern experimental biology. He worked out ingenious experiments to try to answer the crucial biological problems of the time, such as the role of semen in fertilization and the possibility of artificial fertilization.

Spallanzani's experiments did not, however, seem conclusive to some of his opponents. The believers in the doctrine of spontaneous generation maintained that Spallanzani's prolonged boiling of the nutrient medium and his subsequent sealing of the vessel had destroyed some mysterious vital principle in the air and prevented more of it from coming into his vessels from the outside. This airborne principle, they claimed from no specific evidence whatever, was essential for spontaneous generation of microorganisms. And so the doubt remained until the next century, when Louis Pasteur (1822–1895) evolved the ingenious experiment of boiling the nutrients in open-ended swan-neck flasks. The curves of the neck of the flask would allow fresh air to enter but would trap all the dust and particles of various kinds in the air at the bottom of the curve. Pasteur thus showed that it was not air but what was carried in the air, the "germs" of the microorganisms themselves, which caused the nutrient broth to decay.

For a long time microbiology remained the battleground for ideas about spontaneous generation, and it was not until the work of Pasteur that microorganisms, however they arose, were shown to have an important role in the great chemical changes accompanying fermentation and, even more important, to be the causative agents of infectious diseases. There is a direct line in Pasteur's work from his early interest in chemistry to his interest in spontaneous generation and fermentation, to his final proposal of the germ theory of disease. The techniques by which the controversies over spontaneous generation were decided were in principle the same by which he made his great contributions to medical microbiology.

As early as the seventeenth century and before, men had conjectured that infectious diseases might be caused by "living contagions," but the whole matter remained in the realm of theory for two hundred years. In 1835 an Italian lawyer and amateur scientist, Agostino Bassi (1773–1857), had shown that a silkworm disease called muscardine was caused by a parasitic fungus and had conjectured that other diseases were caused by similar parasites of microscopic dimensions, but his discoveries did not attract much attention. Nevertheless, the possibility of such being the case was more and more widely entertained during the first half of the nineteenth century.

Pasteur had begun his earliest scientific work as a chemist and had made a classic series of experiments showing that tartaric acid consisted of two kinds of crystals, those which rotated light to the left and those which rotated it to the right. Since tartaric acid was found in wine vats, it was quite natural that when the French wine industry was suffering great losses through wine turning sour, they should have called in Pasteur to assist them. We shall consider his study of fermentation in more detail later on, since it initiated the final version of the debate between vitalists and mechanists, but his studies conclusively showed that the fermentation which made wine from grape juice and the fermentation which made it turn sour were produced by different microorganisms. If the wine were heated before it could turn sour, the bacteria that caused souring would be killed and the wine would remain intact.

This contribution was so useful that when the silk industry of France was severely threatened by a silkworm disease called pebrine, Pasteur was again summoned to assist his country. Pasteur identified a tiny microorganism as the cause of the disease and showed that it was transmitted to the worms by infected mulberry leaves. He urged the destruction of all infected trees and worms and restocking with healthy ones. His advice was taken and the industry recovered.

On the basis of this and further work Pasteur became convinced that infectious diseases are caused by microorganisms. Although there was much resistance to this idea in many medical and scientific circles, Pasteur received enough support and interest to begin to affect public hygiene. Indeed, it was his work which induced Sir Joseph Lister (1827–1912) to introduce antisepsis (1865) into surgical procedures. Pasteur was convinced of the germ theory of infectious disease before he did any work on animal pathology. It was only in 1877 that he began to study anthrax and in 1879 that he started his work on chicken cholera, two serious diseases, the former mainly affecting sheep but the latter infectious to other animals besides chickens.

Pasteur had long known, as indeed had others, that the first attack of a disease could confer immunity against a second attack, and he was profoundly interested in the debate then going on over vaccination against smallpox. Long before, in 1796, Edward Jenner (1749–1823), an English physician, had shown that a human being who contracted cowpox, a common disease of cattle, would afterwards be immune to the far more virulent disease of smallpox. Jenner had learned this from country people who insisted that anyone who had had cowpox, a mild illness, would be forever protected against the ravages of smallpox. Jenner had the appropriate degree of scientific humility not to dismiss these stories out of hand. For many years he pondered the question and observed that the ignorant peasants might be right. After much hesitation, he thought it safe to try an experiment. He infected a young boy, James Phipps, with cowpox and six weeks later inoculated him with smallpox lymph. Young Phipps did not contract the dread disease. In spite of considerable opposition, vaccination spread and smallpox was on its way to virtual extinction.

The debate over vaccination which raged in Pasteur's time hinged on the question of whether cowpox was really an attenuated version of smallpox or a different disease altogether. Jenner had thought that cowpox was really a weakened form of smallpox, and Pasteur was inclined to agree. Pasteur's great contribution of the development of vaccination through the use of attenuated forms of the microorganisms that cause the disease in question began in an accidental discovery. While working on chicken cholera, he found that isolated cultures of the bacillus would, over a period of time, gradually lose their capacity to produce the disease. In 1879, after his summer vacation, he returned to his laboratory and injected some healthy chickens with cultures which had been growing over the summer. To his disappointment, the chickens failed to get the disease; the cultures were evidently too old. He otbained a new culture from a natural outbreak of the disease and injected it into new animals as well as the ones who had failed to fall sick from the old cultures. Astonishingly enough, the uninjected animals all became ill while most of those previously injected with old cultures failed to contract the disease. Pasteur immediately saw that he had discovered powerful evidence for the principle Jenner had maintained. He had developed a vaccine against chicken cholera by, in effect, creating a weakened version of the disease.

At about the time that Pasteur was beginning to turn to the study of animal diseases, a younger contemporary of his, a German country doctor named Robert Koch (1843–1910), had isolated the anthrax bacillus and learned to culture it. The appearance of Koch's paper in 1876 stimulated Pasteur's interest in the disease, but, deflected by the problem of chicken cholera, he did not devote his full attention to it until about 1880. By 1881 he had developed a vaccine against anthrax along the same principles as those he learned of in his studies of chicken cholera. In a remarkable field trial of the vaccine, he gave dramatic proof of the efficacy of his methods and theories. Pasteur went on to the famous studies of rabies and the development of a vaccine against this otherwise fatal disease, and this work occupied the remaining years of his life.

Meanwhile Koch, who had worked on his own in a home laboratory with improvised equipment, came to the attention of the leading bacteriologist of his time, Ferdinand Cohn (1828–

1898), who greeted his work with enthusiasm and launched him on a research career in Berlin. To Koch we owe the isolation of the tubercle bacillus and the cholera vibrio, as well as many of the fundamental techniques and procedures of the bacteriological laboratory.

The brilliant achievements of nineteenth- and twentieth-century microbiology belong more to the history of medicine than to the history of biological thought. From the biological point of view, the work of Pasteur and Koch established the fundamental principles on which the work of their successors rests. Indeed, everything after them seems like the inevitable consequences of the splendor of their discoveries. The discovery that insects carry diseases, the work in immunology begun so brilliantly by Paul Ehrlich (1854–1915), even the discovery of nutritional diseases caused by the lack of vital food elements, all rest on the methods and principles that these remarkable investigators contributed.

While the work on spontaneous generation and on decay and fermentation led directly into the germ theory of disease and modern medical microbiology, fermentation and the physiological process thought to be its twin, digestion, led in another direction, toward the biochemical understanding of living processes. As we have seen, Borelli and Sylvius left two alternative and mutually exclusive theories of digestion to posterity, the former a strictly mechanical theory and the latter a chemical theory which interpreted digestion as a form of fermentation.

The decision between these two theories did not come until about 1752, with the experiments of a French scientist, René de Réaumur (1683–1757). A brilliant entomologist, Réaumur became interested in the problem of digestion and devised an ingenious way of determining whether the stomach digests food by simply grinding it down to a homogeneous liquid, or whether the stomach juices ferment the food. He placed meat in metal cylinders covered with wire mesh at both ends and made his pet kite swallow them. Why a kite? Because he knew that these birds readily throw up what they cannot digest and the problem of retrieving the tubes would thus be simplified. Later, after the kite died, Réaumur turned to chickens and other fowl, from which the tubes had to be retrieved by a thread, but he certainly picked the right animal in the first instance.

It is obvious that such tubes would make any mechanical action on the meat by the stomach impossible but would readily permit the gastric juices to reach the meat. After retrieving the tube, Réaumur found that part of the meat had dissolved. Many investigators would perhaps have stopped at this point, but Réaumur wanted to make his demonstration foolproof. He then introduced a sponge into the kite's stomach, retrieved it, squeezed out the stomach juices on some meat—and again the meat began to dissolve. Digestion could take place without the stomach at all!

What strikes us about this experiment is its simplicity and conclusiveness. It could have been performed at any time in the history of civilization, but it took Réaumur to do it. This fact illustrates a very important principle in the history of science: experiments are ways of answering questions. What is of crucial importance in the history of experimentation is not simply that the questions be framed, but that they be framed in the right way. As we have seen, two theories of digestion had been current for decades, the one mechanical, the other chemical. Réaumur was confronted therefore with two alternatives and brilliantly devised an experiment to decide between them. Although he was no closer to understanding the precise nature of the chemical processes actually involved, he was able to eliminate one erroneous hypothesis and place the study of digestion on the right track.

An English contemporary of Réaumur, Stephen Hales (1677–1761), was the founder of plant physiology and made brilliant applications of the chemical and phyiscal knowledge of his time to the elucidation of plant life. His book *Vegetable Staticks* (1727) is a record of many ingenious and simple experiments, some of which are still performed in botany courses, all explaining the life of plants in physical terms. He measured root pressure, the force of the upward current of sap, measured the difference between the amount of water absorbed by the roots and that given off by the leaves in transpiration, and was the first to demonstrate that something in the atmosphere contributes to the plant substance itself. We know that this is carbon dioxide, but little was known in Hales's time about the composition of the atmosphere. It was only in his own lifetime that the work of Robert Boyle (1627–1691) began to shake chemistry from its alchemical torpor, and it was not until after his death that Joseph Priestley (1733–1804) discovered oxygen (1774) and Antoine Lavoisier (1743–1794) identified nitrogen as an element, what he called "mofette" a little later. Hales applied his brilliant skills also to the study of what we might call "animal staticks" and was the first to conceive of blood pressure and to measure it. He noted that blood pressure varies from species to species, that it is different in the veins and in the arteries, and that it varies with the state of health of the heart itself.

Respiration had long been a puzzling problem in physiology. Ancient theories connected it with "cooling" and with the elimination of impurities from the venous blood. It was also necessary, we may recall, to introduce air into the blood in order to make the "vital spirit" so necessary in Galen's physiology. Little progress in understanding the nature of respiration was made until Lavoisier. This greatest chemist of modern times gave the first *precise* chemical account of a biological process. Until chemistry had advanced to the point that he took it, it would have been impossible to even begin to understand respiration. Lavoisier, in a series of exact and conclusive experiments, had shown that combustion is the chemical combination of whatever is burning with the oxygen of the atmosphere. Together with the great mathematician Pierre Simon de Laplace (1749–1827), Lavoisier then showed that respiration is a form of combustion. A burning candle or a living mouse, covered by a jar, will produce exactly the same changes in the atmosphere, namely the disappearance of oxygen and the production of carbon dioxide. From these identical effects Lavoisier concluded that respiration must be a form of combustion, and that both the burning candle and the breathing mouse produced heat by an identical process. Far from "cooling," respiration actually made heat!

Lavoisier had shown that respiration was a chemical process which involved the release of energy. At least to this degree, living things were chemical systems and some of their chemical processes, at any rate, were in principle no different from processes which occur outside any organism. Combustion was familiar enough as a source of heat, but soon it was going to be used as a source of power. Subsequent developments in physics and engineering eventually led to the formulation of the law of the conservation of energy. This states that forms of energy may be converted into one another—heat into light or light into heat, for example—but that the total amount of energy in these transactions will be constant. Combustion obviously came under such a law, and if respiration and combustion were really one and the same, then life itself was governed by the law of conservation of energy. It is now almost common sense that we get energy from food and that plants get energy from the sun, but the demonstration of these facts was the work of some of the greatest minds of the nineteenth century. Lavoisier had shown that chemical equations "balanced" and had prepared the way for the further notion that energy relations in chemical changes "balanced" also. The laws of chemical and physical change which governed the burning of a candle governed life itself.

Brilliant and convincing as the work of Lavoisier was, there still remained in the minds of many chemists grave doubts as to the precise nature of the chemicals in living things. Granted that the body was a chemical system and that respiration was a process like combustion, was there not a radical difference between chemical substances derived from living things and those derived from nonliving things? Although it was quite possible to break organic substances up into inorganic constituents, it did not seem possible to do the reverse. Many believed that only a living thing could make inorganic substances and that some particular and unique sort of vital power, possessed only by living things, was indispensable for making the chemicals of life.

The first blow to this conception came through a famous accident in the history of chemistry. A German chemist, Friedrich Wöhler (1800–1882), when only twenty-eight years old, heated lead cyanate with "liquid ammonia." While purifying the result, he obtained some white crystals which he found were identical with urea, a substance already known and hitherto obtainable only from the urine of mammals. Some historians of science have claimed for Wöhler what he did not claim for himself, that he shattered the distinction between organic and inorganic chemistry and laid to rest the notion that a *vis vitalis*, a power of life, was necessary for the synthesis of organic chemicals. In a letter to the great Swedish chemist Jöns Jakob Berzelius (1779–1848) written on February 22, 1848, all Wöhler claimed was that while he could make urea without a kidney, he did need organic substances to make the cyanate and the ammonia which went into the reaction. What he did prove was more like what Réaumur proved, that certain reactions which take place in the body can go on outside it. The first truly organic synthesis, that of acetic acid, was performed in 1843 by Hermann Kolbe, one of Wöhler's students, and it was not until a decade or so later that a French chemist, Pierre Marcelin Berthelot (1827–1907), finally dismissed vitalism in organic chemistry and successfully maintained that "chemistry is one." In a series of brilliant experiments, he was able to synthesize from strictly inorganic components a whole series of organic chemicals, acetylene, benzene and alcohol among others.

After Berthelot, organic chemistry was redefined as the chemistry of carbon compounds, and by the beginning of the twentieth century many organic chemicals had been synthesized and a host of new ones created. In spite of all this progress, it still seemed hopelessly difficult to synthesize the more complex carbohydrates, fats, and the extremely complex proteins which had been identified as the chief constituents of living tissue. The major advances in understanding the protein molecule have been the work of our own time, but the nineteenth-century chemists prepared the way by showing that the very complex substances which make up living things could be broken down into smaller units.

The last major battle over vitalism was fought over fermentation. Justus von Liebig (1803–1873), one of the great chemists of the nineteenth century, had maintained that fermentation was a purely chemical process and that it was a good example of the kind of reaction involving complex chemicals found in living things which could take place at low temperatures. Liebig, like other chemists of his time, was concerned with the problem which was the legacy of Lavoisier's demonstration that respiration is a form of combustion. If the fuel for respiration, for "biological combustion," so to speak, was the carbohydrates and fats, how were they consumed at such a low and constant temperature? This and other chemical reactions which went on in living things could not be duplicated in the laboratory except at temperatures fatal to life. We now know that enzymes, complex protein molecules, act as catalysts and permit reactions to go on at low temperatures and at controlled rates. As early as 1836 Berzelius, who coined the term, had recognized the existence of "catalysts," substances which facilitate reactions without themselves entering into them, in the realm of inorganic chemistry, and had even suggested that enzymes (then called "ferments") might be a special class of catalyst. No one, however, pursued his suggestion for many years. Indeed, it was not until a few decades ago that enzymes were conclusively shown to be proteins.

It is clear that Liebig, working pretty much in the dark, was trying to find some clue to understanding biochemical reactions without appeal to vitalistic principles, and he seized on fermentation. Biochemical processes, in his view, were simply chemical processes of a high order of complexity. With enough knowledge, they could be made to take place in the test tube, without the presence of anything living.

Liebig's approach was challenged from an unexpected quarter. Louis Pasteur, in 1856, began to study fermentation at the behest of the winemakers of France, who were suffering serious losses from wine turning sour. He examined both wine and beer microscopically, knowing that both if properly fermented contained small yeast cells, and found that sour wine and beer contained microorganisms of a very different type. He was able to show that one type of microorganism produced alcohol and the other type soured the beverage. He noted, moreover, that the alcohol-producing organisms worked first and more rapidly than the ones which spoiled the wine, and realized that if the wine were heated at just the right time so as to kill all the organisms, it would be both saved from further fermentation and preserved from spoiling. Pasteur's advice worked and the wine industry was spared great losses.

Pasteur's researches were very convincing and his conclusions seemed to show that fermentation would not occur except through the agency of a living organism. But his fine studies had the effect of deepening the gulf between the chemistry of living organisms and the chemistry of nonliving matter.

It was not until many years later, in 1896, that a German chemist, Eduard Buchner (1860–1917), got unexpected results in some experiments he was engaged in. He was interested in the possible therapeutic uses of proteins and protein fractions, and was trying to obtain a cell-free extract of the protein in yeast. He therefore ground up yeast with fine sand, so that all of the cells would be crushed, and extracted a yeast juice after filtering the mixture. He wanted to preserve this small quantity of juice from decay without altering it chemically, and hit upon the housewives' technique of adding a lot of sugar to it. He discovered to his astonishment that the sugar fermented exactly as if yeast had been growing in it.

Further experiments showed that not only the yeast extract but dead yeast cells would ferment sugar. Whatever it was in yeast that fermented sugar would do so whether the yeasts were alive or dead. Fermentation could take place without the agency of a living organism. The word "enzyme" means "in yeast," and it was because of this discovery that it came to replace the older word "ferment." It had been coined in 1878, long before Buchner's discovery.

Actually various "ferments" had been isolated and studied in the nineteenth century and some scientists had begun to suspect that they were to biological processes what the catalysts of Berzelius were to other chemical processes. It was also clear that some of these ferments would function outside the body—pepsin, for example—but it also seemed equally clear that others required the living cell or organism. In fact, until Buchner's discovery, many chemists distinguished between "organized ferments," which required the living cell, and unorganized ferments," which could function without it. It seemed that fermentation was a solid example of the work of an "organized ferment." After Buchner's contribution, however, a crucial bastion of vitalism had fallen. Some chemists, yielding this fortress, retreated to the one called the protein molecule, and for some time it seemed as if the protein molecule would not yield to analysis or synthesis. The progress of biochemistry in our own time has taken that bastion and no investigator today would argue that there is any biochemical process which in principle requires appeal to anything vitalistic for its elucidation.

iv *The Origin and Development of Living Things*

The long controversy over spontaneous generation was an attempt to answer, however confusedly, the question of where living things come from, in the sense of how life originated. Some, like Aristotle, thought that all the higher organisms had existed from eternity just as they now are and that only more primitive forms of life, such as plants and invertebrates, derived from nonliving matter. Some earlier Greek thinkers had speculated that there had been an origin of all species at some early time of the world, "origin" not in the evolutionary sense but in the sense of species coming into being in their present forms. Even today speculations concerning the ultimate origin of life remain quite conjectural, although we have reason for thinking that our conjectures make pretty good sense since they cohere with a great body of unified scientific knowledge. As we shall see, a great deal of scientific advance had to be made, most of it in the last century or so, before we could give any more convincing account of the origin of life than was possible for the early Greek philosophers.

Another sense we give to the question concerning the origin

of life refers to the origin of the individual. Here, at least, the investigator had before his eyes an ongoing process repeated over and over in all of the great variety of living things. Nevertheless, the questions posed by the phenomena of reproduction and development were just as puzzling as those posed by the very origin of life itself. By what process, for example, does the large, complex adult derive from such utterly different beginnings? Why does a hen's egg always give forth a chick and not something else?

In the state of biological knowledge in Aristotle's time and for a long time thereafter, there were two apparently quite contradictory ways of viewing development. Either the individual exists in a preformed state, as a minute miniature, whether in the father's semen or in the mother's womb, and development is really nothing more than growth in size alone, or the individual begins life in a "simple" or undifferentiated state and all of its structures develop from that condition. In this latter view development is not just increase in size but a change from simple to complex as well.

The former view, as we have seen, was the doctrine of preformationism and the latter the doctrine of epigenesis, so called by William Harvey, who was greatly interested in embryology and stoutly defended Aristotle's theories. Aristotle's magnificent observations and his powerful arguments for epigenesis ruled biological thought for many centuries and with considerable justice. Nevertheless, the application of the microscope to biological investigation gave a new lease on life to preformationism with the result that some of the greatest investigators of the seventeenth and eighteenth cenuries were convinced preformationists. Just as the microscope revealed hitherto invisible forms of life which looked as if they might have come into being spontaneously, so it revealed much more structure and shape in the scarcely visible embryo of the early stages of development than had been suspected. Indeed, when the early microscopists examined semen under their crude instruments, some of them thought they saw, curled up in the head of the spermatozoon, like the fetus in the uterus, a minute but completely formed human being, a so-called "homunculus" or "little man."

They conjectured that this little human, implanted in the mother, grew in size until it was ready to be born. The adult individual was in essence never less complex or structured at any time in its existence, only smaller. It did not evolve out of anything simpler. It is worthwhile mentioning that throughout the seventeenth and most of the eighteenth century, the word "evolution" in biological literature does not refer to the origin of species or of life but to the doctrine of epigenesis, which maintained that the fetus "evolved" out of some simpler form. This fact is a good illustration of the care needed in reading historical documents and the ease with which we may be deceived into misunderstanding a theory.

Those early observers who thought they saw a homunculus in the spermatozoon came to be known as "spermists," and they were opposed to others, the "ovists," who thought that the egg contained the completely preformed individual. Leeuwenhoek, who first saw spermatozoa, entered the controversy on the side of the spermists but held the modified view that the homunculus was a miniature embryo. However bitter the controversy became, both spermists and ovists were united in being preformationists and both drew a curious consequence from their preformationists views.

Each miniature and complete homunculus, whether in the egg or the sperm, would be a complete individual and therefore would itself contain either sperm or egg, depending, of course, on its sex. The sperm or egg of the miniature adult would, in turn, contain other minute individuals with sperms or eggs and so on. This was not only a doctrine of "miniaturization" but of what French scholars conveniently call *emboîtement,* smaller and smaller individuals being contained within the other sperms or eggs much like the arrangement of the nests of boxes one sometimes sees in homes furnished in Japanese or Chinese style. This view obviously precludes the evolution or development of the individual out of a simpler condition. All of mankind existed in a miniature state in one or the other of our first parents, depending on whether one was a spermist or an ovist. If the former, Adam was literally the father of all mankind; if the latter, Eve was just as exclusively the mother of mankind.

Another curious consequence of this doctrine should be apparent. Both spermists and ovists agreed in making the role of one or the other parent in procreation virtually superfluous. Of course, it had long been recognized that sexual union was required for the reproduction of most animals, but what exactly happened during fertilization was quite obscure and hotly debated. No one before Leeuwenhoek and his associate Hamm (1677) had ever seen a spermatozoon, and the mammalian egg was not discovered until 1827 by the Esthonian embryologist Karl von Baer. Regnier de Graaf, between 1668 and 1673, had made careful studies of the generative organs of mammals and discovered the "Graafian" follicle, which contains the egg but which he mistook for the much smaller mammalian egg itself. Although in the opening decades of the nineteenth century it came to be suspected that fertilization involved the fusion of sperm and egg, actual fertilization of an animal egg was not observed until 1879 by Hermann Fol, working with starfish eggs. It is astonishing to reflect that the simple facts of fertilization were a discovery of such relatively recent times.

Earlier theories of fertilization resolved into two views, both of which were advanced in antiquity, one by Aristotle and the other by the followers of the atomist philosopher Democritus. Aristotle, seeking the analogue to the egg in mammals, thought he had found it in an early stage of the embryo when, like an egg, it was surrounded by a membrane. As we have seen, Aristotle believed that this embryo was produced by the mixture of semen, the structure-giving principle, and menstrual blood, the "matter," which coagulated to form it. The semen, while it contributed nothing truly material to the embryo, was the energizing and forming principle and guided epigenetic development. The followers of Democritus, thoroughgoing materialists who held that all of reality was made up of tiny particles, or "atoms," contended that the embryo was formed from two "seeds," that both the father and the mother contributed particles which came together to form the embryo in roughly equal material contributions, and that the embryo was completely formed at conception, although in miniature. Whatever deficiencies they otherwise had, both of these theories had the merit of making both parents necessary for reproduction. The preformationists, on the other hand, whether spermists or ovists, really made sexual union biologically unnecessary and made the simplest, most obvious facts of heredity quite inexplicable. Indeed, the spermists were prepared to argue that if a child resembled its mother the cause was to be found in some kind of unexplained prenatal influence of the mother on the developing embryo. The ovists similarly advanced equally obscure conjectures to account for paternal traits in a child. Spermists thought that the mother was simply a kind of feeding pouch, which the ovists argued that the semen simply started the little ovarian homunculus on its increase in size.

Naive preformationism, with its absurd theories of an endless series of smaller and smaller miniatures of adults, its *emboîtement* of individuals within individuals, seems so wild to us that we can scarcely imagine anyone seriously holding these views. Yet the preformationists were struck with the one crucial question that epigenesis did not really answer: What, after all, is in the egg of a hen, for example, which leads that egg to hatch into a chick and nothing but a chick? It did not explain much to appeal to formative powers in the semen, as the Aristotelians did, although it was perhaps wiser to leave the answer to this problem obscure and get on with observations than to posit the extravagant forms of preformationism. Preformationism was, in the state of knowledge of the time, a respectable position to take if not pushed to absurdity. If it had its difficulties, so did epigenesis, and men of the highest intellectual caliber were ranked on either side of the question. With our recently won knowledge of the molecular basis of heredity, we can mediate between the truth of preformation and the truth of epigenesis. The adult pre-exists in the simpler and smaller fertilized egg as the "information" necessary to produce the adult through the process of growth and development. The manifold genes in the nucleus of the cell control the manufacture of those proteins which make up the structure of living things and which, as enzymes, control the biochemical reactions required for life.

One moral to draw from this story of the conflict between the proponents of epigenesis and those of preformation is that important work is frequently done by those who do not try to answer every question all at once, no matter how crucial. The facts of observation supported epigenesis, and though the question of why an individual breeds true to its species was surely a crucial one, it made good scientific sense to ignore the problem and get on with describing what could be seen, or to attribute the fact to some special form-conferring power in the semen or the egg which shaped the embryo to its species. Obviously, such an explanation explains nothing, but in the history of thought it has often proved advantageous not to try to explain too much. Francis Bacon warned that one of the great impediments to the advancement of learning is that the mind of man is far too ready to impose its patterns of explanation or of order on reality, avoiding the painstaking work of patient inquiry and unwilling to admit that we may die in our own ignorance and must, whether we like it or no, leave the treasure of certain truths to our posterity to discover.

It should be clear that even a preliminary solution to the problems of developmental biology awaited a more profound analysis of the actual structure of organisms, awaited in fact the formulation of the cell theory of the organization of living things. This theory, as we shall see, did not take definitive shape until about 1838, but important preliminary work took place which extended knowledge of developmental processes and organic structures.

Aristotle's great observations on the development of the animal embryo were not matched for plants until the work of a young German physiologist, Kaspar Wolff (1733–1794), who made a careful study of the growth of plants. He noted that the growing tip of the shoots of plants was made up of quite generalized and undifferentiated tissue which gradually differentiated itself into flower and leaf. Turning later on to animals, he showed that organs took form in a relatively undifferentiated embryo through a gradual process of development. The great mass of evidence in favor of epigenesis was thus extended to include the plant world.

As it became clear that organs were formed in the process of development out of simpler structures, attention naturally turned to the components of organs. It is an astonishing fact that the founder of histology, the study of the tissues which make up various organs, worked entirely without the use of a microscope. He felt that the crude instruments available would be more confusing than helpful. A French physician, Marie François Xavier Bichat (1771–1802), in the relatively few years allotted to him of life not only noted that organs were made up of different kinds of material but gave these materials the name we still use, "tissue."

The next question that might be asked should be clear enough: If organs are made of tissues, what are tissues made of? Even a green student of biology today would answer "cells," but here again there was a long process of development before the cell theory was definitely formulated. As we have seen, in the seventeenth century Robert Hooke had examined a thin slice of cork through his microscope and seen what looked like a latticework of empty chambers. These he called "cells," after the Latin word for room. Other observers like Grew had noted the similar structure of plant sections, and still others in the course of time had noted some sort of analogous organization in animal tissues, but these remained mere data of observation and were not understood as fundamental structures. Hooke had described cells, correctly for his specimen, as empty chambers surrounded by a "diaphragm," which we would call the cell wall, and until the opening years of the nineteenth century this was the only generally recognized and defined cell structure. From that time, more and more observers began to notice that the cells of freshly killed tissues were filled with a gelatinous or mucilaginous substance which, with the microscopes and techniques available—limited, although better than Hooke's or Grew's equipment—seemed uniform and homogeneous.

Cells and the "cellular juice" they contained came to be advanced as the basic structural units of living organisms in a tentative fashion by various investigators during the thirties of the nineteenth century, and there are hints of the theory even earlier. In 1831 Robert Brown (1773–1858) described the nucleus of plant cells and recognized them as a normal feature of such cells. The nuclei of the blood cells of fish had actually been described earlier by Leeuwenhoek and later microscopists, who could not, with their instruments and techniques, detect them elsewhere.

In 1835 a French protozoologist, Félix Dujardin (1801–1860), observed the structure of amoeboid protozoa and came to the conclusion that the contents of these organisms, which he called "sarcode" from the Greek word for flesh, was a perfectly "homogeneous, contractile, diaphanous and gelatinous substance, insoluble in water and without any sign of organization." Or so it seemed with the instruments at his disposal. Dujardin, in effect, argued that the amoeba was a simple organism, a sack of "sarcode" irreducible to any similar structure. The simplest form of life was a kind of living jelly.

In 1838 a German protozoologist, Christian Gottfried Ehrenberg (1795–1876), countered this view and argued that far from being simple, the protozoa were complex organisms with a system of organs quite like those of higher animals. It is not insignificant that Ehrenberg worked with ciliates like the paramecium which, even with the microscopes then available, had much more apparent structure and complexity than the amoeba.

This debate over whether or not protozoa were simple, undifferentiated organisms was really over the degree of complexity of the simplest living things and extended even into our own century. Protozoologists long argued that the protozoa were really "acellular" animals and that there was no close analogy between them and the cells of tissues. With modern electron microscopy we can see that most of these debates were either a quibbling over definition or an indication of simple ignorance of the extraordinary structural complexity of even the so-called simple cells, whether protozoan or metazoan. Not only are protozoa cells in a perfectly sensible meaning of the term, but they share all of the essential structures of somatic cells and have a few of their own besides which they require for independent existence. While Dujardin was undoubtedly influenced by then current notions of cell structure, the cell theory was not formally and explicitly applied to protozoa until 1845 by Karl von Siebold (1804–1885) after the work of the two great German proponents of cell theory, the botanist Matthias Jakob Schleiden (1804–1881) and the physiologist Theodor Schwann (1810–1882).

Schleiden, in 1838, maintained that enough evidence had been accumulated to show that all plants were built up of cells. His work, unlike the numerous anticipations of cell theory—by Lamarck some thirty years earlier, for example—was marked by full and articulate awareness of the significance of the cell as a fundamental structural unit. He also grasped the significance of Robert Brown's observations of the cell nucleus in plants. Brown was a distinguished scientist, famous for his elucidation of the sexual processes of higher plants, for his discovery of the "Brownian movement" of colloidal particles, and for his microscopic observations of fossil plants. With his rich and versatile scientific mind he attempted to describe some function for the nuclei he first discovered in the outer layers of the tissues of orchids and certain Australian plants similar to our periwinkles. He soon realized that nuclei were a regular feature of plant cells, and attempted to trace the nucleus in the earlier stages of pollen cells and in the young ovum as well as in tissues.

Schleiden agreed with Brown on the importance of the nucleus, which, although it had been observed even before Brown, had been treated as unimportant. It was, in Schleiden's view, an essential element of the cell, for it had some sort of reproductive function. He conjectured that nuclei arose by crystallization out of a structureless fluid which he called the cytoblastema ("cell-bud") and which corresponds roughly to what we might call the cytoplasm of the cell. He then postulated that the cell membrane formed around the nucleus and a portion of the cytoblastema to make the cell. Whatever its inadequacies,

Schleiden's theory of the cell had the merit of recognizing the reproductive function of the nucleus and of trying to account for its origin in terms of what was known about processes like crystallization which are physicochemical in character.

Scarcely a year later came the work of Theodor Schwann, who formulated cell theory for animals. After careful and prolonged microscopic examination of animal tissues, he concluded that all tissues are made of cells or of substances made by cells. He recognized that cells are fundamental units, in that they lead a partially independent existence, although in many respects they are subject to the functioning of the whole organism of which they are parts. Moreover, he noted that all cells possess a membrane which serves to "detach" them from one another. Other observers had already noted the segmentation of fertilized eggs of both invertebrates and mammals, and Schwann correctly concluded from their observations that the egg develops into the young animal by a process of *cell* division. Cells, moreover, are of different kinds, and each of the tissues of an organism is constituted of a different type of cell. Tissues, thus, are formed of cells through the process of cell division.

Schwann's conception of cell division was, of course, far closer to the truth of things than Schleiden's theory that cells arise by a process of nuclear crystallization out of an undifferentiated "cytoblastema." It is odd that though both men came to know each other and each other's views, Schwann did not correct Schleiden's erroneous notion on the origin of cells. Perhaps he did not feel that it was inconsistent with his own account and considered that Schleiden was correct about the *origin* of cells while he himself was correct about the way cells reproduce. It was Karl Nägeli, the Swiss botanist who, as we shall see, was so enthusiastic about Darwin and so unsympathetic to Mendel, who corrected Schleiden's theory.

The full elucidation of the phenomena of cell division, especially the nuclear changes, had to await the work of Eduard Strasburger, a German botanist, and Walther Flemming, a German zoologist. Using vastly improved microscopes and new staining techniques, they created modern cytology. Flemming, as we shall see, gave the most complete and exhaustive account of nuclear changes in cell division and coined the term "mitosis" to describe the process as a whole. He also invented some of the basic terminology of its various constitutent phases.

In spite of the numerous anticipations of cell theory, Schleiden and Schwann deserve the credit for propounding the theory in complete and essentially definitive form. Schwann especially had a host of important ideas on the morphological and physiological properties of cells. He was the first to draw a distinction between what he called the "plastic" phenomena of cells, their structure, and their "metabolic" phenomena, their physiology. In his emphasis on the physiological properties of cells, their capacity for growth and reproduction, Schwann was well ahead of his predecessors and his contemporaries.

The work of Schleiden and Schwann had immediate repercussion. As we have seen, Von Siebold applied cell theory to our understanding of the protozoa, maintaining that they were single cells, and hard upon this, Ernst Haeckel (1834–1919) divided the animal kingdom into its two great classifications, protozoa and metazoa. The "cellular sap" was renamed protoplasm by the German botanist Hugo von Mohl (1850–1872) in 1846; he borrowed the term from its coiner, the Czech biologist Johannes Purkinje (1787–1869). The latter had used it to describe the earliest detectable stage of the animal embryo; the Greek roots of the word mean "first-formed." Von Mohl, however, used it to refer to the presumably simple gelatinous substance which fills cells. Considerably later, in 1861, Max Schultze (1825–1874) brought together various notions of his predecessors, that something called "protoplasm" was the stuff of life, that protozoa were single cells and that "sarcode" must be protoplasm, that—as Karl Gegenbaur had maintained in the same year—the eggs of vertebrates must be considered single cells, and came up with what was to be called the protoplasm theory of life. This theory was a generalization of the earlier theories about life substance and described the cell as a well-defined mass of protoplasm enclosed in a membrane and surrounding a nucleus.

A further generalization of cell theory was the work of the founder of modern pathology, the German physician Rudolf Virchow (1821–1902). In 1858 he applied the cell theory to the understanding of disease processes and showed that the process of disease took place in the cells and tissues of the afflicted organism. In a brief Latin phrase, *omnis cellula e cellula,* "each cell from another cell," he epitomized the end of the earlier hypotheses that cells might arise from simpler states through processes like crystallization or accretion around a nucleus.

Virchow was a remarkable and versatile scholar, active in liberal causes, and perhaps the most famous physician of his era. He played a curious and mistaken role in the controversy over the nature of the Neanderthal skull when that famous bit of bone was discovered in 1856. He was the greatest pathologist of his time and his erroneous opinion, that the skull was recent and that its peculiar structure was the result of disease, carried great weight. It was the contrary opinion of Paul Broca (1824–1880), a distinguished French surgeon and researcher in neuroanatomy, that soon prevailed, however.

Until cell theory reached a high degree of sophistication, the nature of the most fundamental biological phenomena, fertilization, differentiation, development, was doomed to remain unintelligible. The gap could only be filled with the less extravagant versions of preformationism at best, and at worst with fantasies about unnecessary fathers or mothers which would interest a modern psychoanalyst more than anyone else.

The man who did most to place developmental biology on a cellular basis, although anticipated in this approach by others, was a remarkable Swiss histologist and embryologist, Rudolf von Kölliker (1817–1905). In 1841, while still a young man, he had demonstrated that spermatozoa are cellular products and originate in the organism, and in 1844 he demonstrated the same for the ovum. For a long time a good many investigators had thought that spermatozoa were parasitic microorganisms, and though this belief was waning, it was Von Kölliker who really gave it the deathblow. He further maintained that the organism develops from the ovum through the process of cell division, and that this process involves the differentiation of cells into different types. Moreover, he gave convincing evidence that the fertilized ovum as well as the unfertilized ovum must be considered a single cell. He also brilliantly conjectured that the nucleus transmitted hereditary qualities, and even thought of "mutations" as the way in which species might change.

While Von Kölliker was applying cell theory to the facts of reproduction, Karl Ernst von Baer (1792–1876), who had discovered the mammalian egg within the Graafian follicle, was placing embryology on a comparative basis. A convinced adherent of epigenesis, he showed that the organs of the developing embryo were differentiated out of layers of tissue which he called "germ layers," as we still do today. A contemporary German physician, Robert Remak (1815–1865), established the number of germ layers at three and gave them the names we still use: ectoderm, mesoderm, endoderm. (It was Remak who also was the first to witness amitotic division of a cell, the type of cell division characteristic of many protozoa, where the nucleus does not arrange itself into chromosome structures before dividing.)

By the time Von Kölliker was beginning his work, he and other contemporary biologists were convinced that fertilization involved the fusion of ovum and sperm to form a "zygote," or fertilized egg. As we have seen, fertilization was not witnessed until Hermann Fol saw it take place in a starfish egg in 1879. Nevertheless, between the 1840s and Fol's time a great deal of evidence had been accumulated to support the fusion theory of fertilization. As early as 1824 two French investigators, Prévost and Dumas, had completed the work begun by Lazzaro Spallanzani in the late eighteenth century and had shown that the sperm was not only necessary to fertilization but could fertilize the egg without the seminal fluid it originally came in, the fluid which many thinkers had believed was the essential trigger of embryonic development.

Shortly before Fol's observation, in 1876, Oskar Hertwig (1849–1922) had foreseen that the result of penetration by the sperm would be nuclear fusion. He detected two nuclei in a recently fertilized egg and correctly assumed that one came from the sperm. At a slightly later time after fertilization he noted that the ovum had only one nucleus, as if it had not been fertilized. At a still later stage, he noted two nuclei again, just prior to the division of the ovum. All this was clear evidence that fertilization, the formation of the zygote, involved the union of two nuclei, the so-called pronuclei, one from the female gamete or egg and the other from the male gamete or sperm.

But well before all of these observations on the cellular basis of reproduction were in, Von Kölliker was embarked on the twenty-year task of placing the magnificent embryological contributions of Von Baer and Remak on a cellular basis. He made good use of the contributions Von Baer had made to comparative embryology. The latter had noted that the embryos of different species resemble each other much more than the adults of those same species and that the resemblance is stronger the earlier the stage of the embryo. Von Kölliker pointed out that the changes which took place in development, in epigenesis, must be changes in the structure and organization of cells. It was because the progress from simple to complex was matched by progressively greater differentiation of cells and tissues that the earlier and simpler stages of embryonic life resembled each other more than the later stages.

Von Baer's contribution to embryology in its theoretical aspect was the most important one of his time and can be summed up in his formulation of the "biogenetic" law, a general statement about all embryological development whatsoever. It can be stated as three propositions:

1. General characters of the embryo appear before special characters and less general, or special, characters develop out of more general characters.

2. Animals of different species begin embryological development by resembling each other closely and then diverge more and more in the course of development.

3. A higher animal passes through stages in development which resemble stages in the embryological development of the lower animals.

This last proposition is most important to understand

properly. It is not the notion of recapitulation, whether connected with evolutionary theory or not. Harvey, for example, thought that the embryo of higher animals passed through stages which could be identified with adult forms of lower organisms according to the principle of the ladder of nature. Haeckel thought that ontogeny recapitulated phylogeny, that the embryo passed through ancestral forms of its evolutionary forebears. Von Baer's point, on the other hand, was that a mammalian embryo will pass through stages which resemble identical stages of a chick embryo or a reptilian embryo, not the *adult* forms of these lower organisms.

It was, of course, tempting to enthusiasts for the theory of evolution to seize on embryological data such as the gill-like structures which appear in mammalian embryos at an early stage of development and think of them as recapitulating the fish ancestry of man. Actually, these embryonic structures will turn into quite different organs in a mammalian embryo. In fish they become gills, while in mammals they turn into such structures as the Eustachian tubes, the tonsils and the thymus gland. Tracing out the destiny of the embryonic "gills" of mammals was the work of one of the leading morphologists of the later nineteenth century, the German Karl Gegenbaur (1826–1903).

Embryology, as it progressed, became a field for bold conjectures and fanciful speculations. If Haeckel saw the history of life on earth in the developing embryo, Von Baer, who was opposed to evolution, found all sorts of odd numerical and geometrical relationships between the developing organs of the embryo, so many that his work is more than a little suggestive of a kind of Pythagorean number mysticism. Haeckel was so convinced of the importance of embryology for the elucidation of the mysteries of life and his prestige was so great that he practically turned the study of comparative anatomy into comparative embryology. This was, in a way, an inevitable result of the dominance of evolutionary theory. The naturalist came to be interested in the "history" of the organ and its development as furnishing clues to the historical relations of organisms. The function of the organ became somewhat secondary, so that physiology too came to be sundered from the anatomical study with which it had previously been bound.

As soon as the phenomenon of cell differentiation became clear, the search began for its causes. This problem, still a crucial one today, obviously threw embryologists back on the whole problem of heredity. What makes the apparently identical cells of the earliest cleavage stages of embryonic development gradually arrange themselves into layers which then give rise to different tissues? Moreover, why does the progressive differentiation of the embryo proceed in such a way that it duplicates its own species and no other? If the earliest stages of the embryos of different species resemble each other, the adults certainly do not, so that differentiation must proceed in different ways in different kinds of organisms, however much alike the beginnings of the process may seem.

During the last twenty years of the nineteenth century Wilhelm Roux (1850–1924), a German biologist, advanced the notion that the fertilized egg should be thought of as a complex, highly structured mechanism composed of "determinants" (the word is his) of various types of tissues which were parceled out to the cells during egg cleavage. These determinants were structures, and were responsible for differentiation itself. After a sufficient number of cleavages had taken place, we would find the determinants for different tissues segregated into different cells, one for muscle cells in one cell, one for nerve cells in another and so on. Each of the cells in which these determinants were isolated would then become the parents of the respective tissues whose determinants they contained.

This view of differentiation was shared by August Weismann (1834–1914), a great theoretical biologist whose famous theory of "germ plasm" postulated the continuity of heredity material from parents to offspring. According to Weismann, germ plasm alone was immortal, and only germ plasm, carried in germ cells, continued from generation to generation, all the body cells being doomed to extinction. Moreover, germ plasm was not modifiable by any environmental factors. Any variation in species was due to particles of germ plasm which he called "ids," the fundamental units of heredity, rearranging themselves.

Chromosomes, the fine threadlike structures which appear in the cell nucleus during cell division, had been intensively studied after new microscopical techniques had rendered them visible to investigators. Their function, however, was a matter of conjecture. Weismann brilliantly guessed that the chromosomes were the vehicles of germ plasm and carried the ids, each of which, he believed, in turn carried all of the determinants necessary for the development of a complete individual. Weismann also brilliantly anticipated the discovery of meiosis, the reduction division by which the number of chromosome in the sex cells, sperm and ova, is half the regular number of chromosomes in other kinds of cells. He surmised that the number of hereditary factors or structures must remain constant from generation to generation if there was to be continuity in any species. Unless each of the sex cells carried half the factors of heredity, the number of such factors would double with each generation instead of remaining constant. If the chromosomes were the carriers of all the hereditary "data," they could scarcely double their number in each generation without crowding all other structures out of the cell!

Roux's determinants might be regarded as the fundamental structures making up Weismann's ids, and Roux proceeded to test his theory in some experiments which, however ironic the final outcome, must be considered the beginning of modern experimental embryology.

Roux destroyed one cell of the two-cell stage of a cleaving frog's egg. The remaining cell developed for a while and grew into something that looked like half an embryo before it died. Roux interpreted this according to his theory of determinants by assuming that all of the determinants for the left-side structures and all those for the right-side structures of the adult had been segregated into two separate cells at the first cleavage. Roux generalized his observations into the so-called mosaic theory of embryonic development. According to this view the early embryo is really a mosaic of cells containing different determinants, so that beginning with the very first cleavage, a particular cell becomes capable of producing only a specific part of the embryonic tissues and structures. While the fertilized egg is omnipotential—contains all determinants—these are gradually parceled out through successive cleavages, each later cell becoming more and more determined to its special function.

Roux's work attracted great attention among embryologists even though it seemed—in a very sophisticated way, to be sure—to revive some form of preformationism, for in his view the fertilized egg contained all later *structures* in germ. This is quite different from saying, for example, that the fertilized egg contains molecular aggregates which govern biochemical processes which, in turn, differentiate cells into various types. In the latter case what is transmitted is a potentiality for a particular process, while Roux's theory transmitted structural elements of a specific kind.

Other investigators tried to verify Roux's work and they often did obtain results similar to his own. Considerably later, however, it was found that Roux's results were brought about by allowing the killed cell of the two-cell stage to remain in contact with the live one. The dead cell's products prevented the live one from developing naturally. A two-cell stage of a frog embryo from which one cell was *removed* would give quite different results. The remaining cell would develop into a normal embryo, somewhat smaller than usual, but not the abnormal organism Roux had interpreted as being a half-embryo.

Even before this was demonstrated, another investigator, working with sea urchin's eggs, had shown that the mosaic theory of development, if it applied to frogs, certainly did not apply to sea urchins. Hans Driesch (1867–1941), an eminent German biologist, separated the cells of the two-cell stage in sea urchin's eggs and got two complete larvae of half the normal size. In subsequent experiments he was able to get complete larvae from the single cells of later stages of segmentation up until the thirty-two-cell stage, perfectly normal embryos in every respect except that they were one thirty-second of normal size! For a time, until Roux's experiments were shown to be misleading, there were two theories of embryonic development, the mosaic theory of Roux and one called "regulative" to describe the results of Driesch's experiments. These theories were both assumed to be true but to apply to different organisms. Progress in cytology, meanwhile, was making Roux's theory less and less convincing. The nuclei of all segmented cells in the embryo were shown to be identical, and if chromosomes, as both Roux and Weismann thought, carried determinants or ids, there was no evidence whatever that embryonic cell division segregated out the different chromosomes which were assumed to carry different determinants.

It was beginning to be apparent that the nuclear material of each cell is identical, that differentiation must be a kind of realization of some of these potentialities to the exclusion of others. How the nuclear material, identical in each cell, nevertheless works to differentiate cells is still a crucial problem of developmental biology and only the barest beginnings have been made in elucidating it.

With the work of Roux and Driesch modern experimental embryology was launched and led to the work of Hans Spemann (1869–1941), one of the most skilled and ingenious experimental biologists in history.

Spemann's initial experiments were meant to take up where Roux and Driesch had left off. Let us recall that Weismann had conceived of the nucleus of the cell as carrying "ids," the units of heredity. He further suggested that the nucleus of the cell of a fertilized egg was to be thought of as constituted of "primordia," units of heredity which controlled the subsequent development of tissues and organs. His use of the word "mosaic" was more than a simple analogy. The primordia were separated from one another in the course of progressive cell divisions much as one might separate the stones of a mosaic picture. Some would go into one cell and others into another until enough divisions had taken place so that the primordia were all distributed. Although they were separated into different cells, Weismann saw them all as working together in exact correlation to produce the finished organism.

It was in the light of this theory that Roux hypothesized

that the embryo at the two-cell stage would have half of the "determinants," as he called Weismann's ids or primordia, and performed his famous experiments on frogs' eggs which led to the mosaic theory of development. Although Roux's experiments were later proved faulty, other organisms were found in which what could actually be called a mosaic pattern of development occurred. Annelid worms, for example, develop according to this pattern; at an early stage of cleavage, the sixth, a cell is formed from which the whole of the mesoderm tissue of the later embryo will develop. Driesch, on the other hand, working with sea urchins, found that every cell of the early stage of the embryo of this organism would produce a complete organism. There seemed, in short, to be two completely different patterns of embryonic development, one called "mosaic" and the other called "regulative."

Now if these two different patterns were caused by a distribution of hereditary elements in the one case and the absence of such distribution in the other, it threw a good deal of the established facts of cytology into confusion. The essential features of all division were the same in all kinds of eggs; the chromosome number was constant in all cells produced in cleavage. What then governed these apparently antithetical patterns of development?

As we shall see, the answer lay in a different direction. To run ahead of our story a little, before the cells of an embryo become differentiated they can develop in different ways. They are then said to be "competent." After they have differentiated and moved sufficiently along some special direction, they are said to lose this competence. We now know what the early investigators did not, that any cell has all of the genetic data it needs to become any type of cell. We also know that, in most cases, the change of a cell from an undifferentiated to a differentiated state is the result of complex external influences. The difference between mosaic and regulative development finally turns out to be the rate at which some embryos differentiate and their cells lose their competence. In mosaic eggs this process, characteristic of all development in any embryo, takes place earlier. Hereditary factors are not distributed or parceled out in either mosaic or regulative development. The embryo that is to develop in a mosaic pattern is mosaic at the start; the one that is to develop in the regulative fashion differentiates on the cellular level later. Different factors of heredity are activated in cells taking different developmental pathways, but each cell has all the factors. Insofar as the mosiac theory of development postulated a distribution of factors, it has been dropped.

Now let us see how Spemann was able to throw fresh light on the concept of development and mediate between the two apparently contradictory theories of development.

With a loop made of hair, Spemann constricted a fertilized salamander egg just as it was about to cleave, leaving only a small, narrow connection between the halves of cytoplasm. One side of the constricted egg contained the nucleus and the other did not. The side with the nucleus continued to cleave while the other side remained unchanged. After the cleaving side had grown big enough, a nucleus from one of the cleaving cells was pushed across the little tunnel of cytoplasm to the side which lacked it. It too then began to cleave. The result was two embryos, the one with the head start developing first and the other finally catching up. In one experiment, Spemann was able to get as many as thirty-two cells on the initially cleaving side before any nuclear material was transferred to the other.

This remarkable experiment showed, apparently, that development was regulative. A nucleus from a cell of the thirty-two-cell stage was able to produce a whole organism. Moreover, Spemann's experiment was more elegant than that of Driesch. He did not separate cleaving cells and have them develop separately, but left the cells connected and still achieved separate, normal embryos. His experiment was tantamount to transplanting the nucleus of a cell from a later stage of the embryo to a cell without a nucleus and getting successful development.

Half of the salamander egg, like that of many organisms, is dark and the other light. Immediately after fertilization a small crescentlike portion of the boundary between the dark and light halves becomes grey. This "grey crescent" appears just before the first cleavage. The first of Spemann's experiments was performed by pinching the egg *across* the grey crescent so that both halves of the pinched egg had some of it. In a second experiment, however, the egg was pinched *parallel* to the grey crescent, so that one half, the half with the nucleus, had all of the grey crescent. The half without the nucleus eventually divided after the nucleated half had grown far enough to push some nuclear material into it. The result, however, was not a normal though retarded embryo, but a so-called "belly-piece" containing cells for liver, lungs and other organs lying in the abdomen but no skeleton or nervous system. In fact, it had no organized structure at all. Spemann attributed this phenomenon to the absence of the "grey crescent" in the embryo.

Spemann hypothesized from these results that the area of the grey crescent acted as a kind of "organizer," that it had some influence of a crucial sort on the subsequent development of the embryo. Development could not be the result of the nucleus acting alone. Under one set of circumstances the nucleus would produce a normal embryo once it moved over to the other half of the constricted embryo, and in another set of circumstances it would not. Clearly, the grey crescent had a crucial role to play in organizing development. Spemann proceeded to test this hypothesis with another set of brilliant experiments.

In the course of the early stages of development, the embryo first turns into a small cluster of cleaving cells and then enters what is called the blastula stage, when the cells are so arranged that the globular embryo possesses an internal cavity. The next stage is called the gastrula stage and, in the process of gastrulation, the embryo undergoes radical reorganization. At the site of the pigmented cells making up the grey crescent a groove, depression or "dimple" appears called the blastopore, and the area just above this pore juts out a bit to form a structure called the dorsal lip. It is through the blastopore that the great changes of this stage take place. All of the cells of the light hemisphere of the egg move to the interior of the egg through the blastopore in a process called invagination. Meanwhile, the cells of the dark half of the embryo grow and spread to cover the entire surface of the embryo. By the time this process is well under way an embryo looks a bit like a ball with one side pushed in a little. Upon completion of these movements the embryo enters the nerula stage, marked by the beginnings of the development of the nervous system.

Since nerve tissue is the first tissue to differentiate and it occurs in the region where the grey crescent first appears and which seemed to be crucial to organized development, Spemann decided to try some experiments with the dorsal lip. What would happen to an embryo if the dorsal lip of another embryo were transplanted to it? Would the transplanted lip "organize"? Would it induce the formation of the tissues which normally derive from that region? It had been known for some time that in the course of normal embryonic development, the lens of the eye is "induced." It begins as a small protuberance, jutting out from the embryo's brain, which then becomes a vesicle. This vesicle apparently induced the skin lying over it to change its character and become a transparent lens. This was a clear-cut instance of an activity like that of the grey crescent. The vesicle changed what would normally have remained skin into material for a lens.

Spemann transplanted a second dorsal lip to the gastrula-stage embryo of a salamander. In order to trace the fate of the second dorsal lip, he took it from a species of salamander which was "colorless" and transplanted it to a salamander which was dark. The region to which he transferred the second lip began to reorganize itself as it normally did and the result was two salamanders connected like Siamese twins. The extra salamander induced by the colorless dorsal lip had tissues of both kinds, dark and colorless. This meant that the transposed dorsal lip had actually influenced the developing cells of the dark salamander to turn colorless. The organizer was able to turn a region of the salamander with presumptive epidermis, tissue which would normally become skin, into nerve tissue, and initiate a whole new development of a second organism. Spemann did not conclude that he had found the key to all of development. His notion of the organizer was not a simple or unitary one. He assumed that there must be many organizers, whatever they were, the one picking up where the other left off.

As we shall see, the hunt for the nature of the organizer proved to lead in very bewildering paths. Dead tissues, numerous chemicals, and even the common laboratory dye methylene blue could work as organizers. It eventually became clear, as a result of these attempts, that there is no master substance in the cells which is responsible for differentiation. It is only during a certain period of development that a tissue is able to react to the organizer stimulus, when it is "competent," and a wide variety of stimuli seem to be able to trigger differentiation. It seems clear that the place to study development is in the interactions of tissues and cells with each other. Development is organized into a plurality of distinct but interacting systems, and each system seems to be so constructed that a normal end-product often results even when the conditions of development have been somewhat abnormal. There are apparently all kinds of self-regulating and compensatory mechanisms at work which suggest "feedback" reactions of a chemical kind. In short, the organizer, as a definable substance, has dissolved into a complex system of actions and reactions.

Experimental embryologists working after Spemann have shown that even if the organizer, whatever it is, may determine what organs are to be formed, the genes will determine the characteristics of those organs. Organizer activity triggers genes but it cannot change them. For example, tissue from a frog embryo which was presumptive flank epidermis was transplanted to the presumptive head of salamander embryo. The latter developed the head suckers of a tadpole instead of the balancers of a salamander and the jaws of a frog instead of the teeth of a salamander! Frog genes produce frog organs even in a salamander! How the genes of one organism can be triggered by the organizer from another is completely obscure.

Other experiments have deepened the complexity of the problems of development. Tissues from embryonic organisms are grown in tissue cultures after having been dissociated so that all of the cells are separate from one another. These cells, even though they have never been adult tissues, will reassemble themselves according to their kind and grow. Such affinities, when understood, may hold a good part of the answer to the problems of development.

Developments and refinements in the techniques of tissue culture first introduced in 1907 by the distinguished American embryologist Ross Harrison (1870–1959) as a method for studying developmental problems, have made it possible to fertilize mammalian eggs in vitro and to study the initial stages of embryonic development with a directness formerly impossible. Advanced techniques and fresh observations may suggest the new ideas developmental biology requires.

This brief survey of the history of man's attempt to understand the nature of fertilization, reproduction and development should show how persistent the re-emergence of old theories is. To be sure, they don't return in the old form, but return they do. After the great results of the second period of brilliant use of the microscope, in the nineteenth century, preformation in the sense of a gamete enclosing a miniature adult was utterly untenable. But Roux's theory of determinants, as we have seen, was preformationism, although in a new and much more sophisticated guise. The ghost of preformationism of a structural kind has finally been laid to rest by modern molecular biology. The truth of preformationism lies in the fact that we inherit, in the form of chemical factors, the "information" for making all of the chemical building-blocks of our bodies. But we do not inherit actual structures, only the capacity to make them. We now know that each cell contains all of the genetic information for making the whole organism even if it doesn't use it all. How then does differentiation take place? How are the capacities we mentioned realized?

Careful study of the giant chromosomes of insect larvae have shown that various sites along the chromosome are chemically more active at one time than at another. This heightened activity is indicated by certain characteristic "puffs" or swellings along the length of the chromosome, and these have been shown to be the sites of increased synthesis of DNA, the controlling chemical in the whole elaborate process of protein synthesis in the cell. In earlier terminology, the genes which are the physical basis of hereditary traits are active at these sites.

What seems to be true is that the determinants of cell differentiation are not parceled out among cells, but are all present in each cell and are *differentially active.* How this differential activity proceeds is the crucial problem. What makes one part of the chromosome biochemically active at the appropriate time, and then shuts off its activity as the particular protein or enzyme whose manufacture it controls is present in sufficient quantity? What starts the activity at another site of the chromosome when another particular protein is needed?

Some investigators think that all of this differential activity is controlled by special genes and is therefore directed from the nucleus where all of the genetic information is contained. Others give great weight to chemical factors in the cytoplasm. It is likely, however, that the differentiation of cells involves quite complex interactions between nucleus and cytoplasm. Analogous processes take place at the tissue level of organization, where it is well known that interaction between groups of differentiated cells is crucial for organ development.

It would seem that just as cell theory opened the door to our basic understanding of the fundamental problems of reproduction and development, modern biochemistry has opened the door to our understanding of cell differentiation and embryonic development. This phase of research is really at its beginnings and its disclosures will doubtless be fascinating. Nevertheless, all of the analytical knowledge that we now have and all yet to come must be, as it were, put together to give us a picture of the developing organism which is not simply a sum of parts.

V *Darwin and Evolution: the Transformations of Life*

Early in the history of ancient Greek thought, philosophers had speculated that all life arose out of inanimate matter at some time in the distant past, and even that there had been some sort of sequential order to the appearance of the varied forms of life. Anaximander of Miletus (611–547 B.C.) conjectured that the first forms of life, simple ones, were generated by the action of the sun on watery ooze which covered some of the as yet unpopulated earth. Fishlike forms next appeared, then land forms with lungs, and finally man. With considerable acuteness, Anaximander realized that man must have come upon the scene later than other animals, because his young need so much care before they can fend for themselves. Some animals, at least, that mature early had to pre-exist man since man depended on such animals for his own existence.

Only fragments and allusions are left of the work of Anaximander, so the full scope of his teaching on the origins of life is unknown to us. Some scholars have thought that he anticipated the modern theory of evolution, namely, that present-day species originated out of simpler forms of life through gradual transformations, in a long historical process. It seems clear, however, that Anaximander was really talking about successive creations of species, not about their descent from other forms. Worms, fish, land animals and man arose, to be sure, in a historical sequence, but they each came into being fully formed. There was, in short, no "descent of man," nor for that matter of any one species from any other.

What is of real importance in Anaximander's theory is that the successive creations he thought had occurred took place over a long period of time with considerable intervals between. That some forms of life had to pre-exist other forms simply because of the nature of their interdependence was an excellent bit of scientific inference. He understood that present conditions among living things contained clues pointing to completely different conditions in the past. Anaximander thus gave to life a history, although it was not the history of life as we now believe it to be.

Another early Greek thinker, Empedocles of Agrigentum (c. 490–430 B.C.), offered an alternative theory concerning the origin of life. Matter, according to Empedocles, was in continual change and acted under the influence of two opposing forces, love and hate, or as we might put it today, attraction and repulsion. At some point in the distant past, matter came together to make not complete organisms but their parts, their limbs and their organs. Bizarre as it may sound, we might imagine, according to this theory, a primeval earth with lungs, livers, hearts, arms, legs and the like all floating in the ooze out of which they originated through the action of the force of love. Through random combinations—and "random" is the important word here—all sorts of parts came together. Most of these combinations would be unable to survive—a lion's limbs on the body of an octopus, for example—and they would die, but those parts that came together in workable combinations would survive, reproduce and populate the earth.

This strange theory is unhistorical, unlike the theory of Anaximander; there are no successive creations of living things. And neither Anaximander's theory nor that of Empedocles allows for the transformation of species. Both attempt to account for the origin of life by assuming that species, however and whenever they arose, did so in their present forms. Empedocles' implausible account of the origin of life does, however, contain the germ of a very important idea: it is the first attempt we know of to account for the *apparently* purposive and *actually* adaptive structures of living things on purely mechanical principles. Starting with parts and chance combinations of parts, what survived was what worked. The result might look as if it had been shaped according to the intelligent planning of a divinity or by an internal, mysterious shaping force, but it was in fact the result of chance. In principle, this is not so utterly far from the modern notion of natural forces acting on random variations to select those best adapted for survival. There is, of course, an enormous gulf between the primitive theory of Empedocles and modern Darwinism, but Darwin himself was delighted to learn of this account of the origin of species according to the operations of chance which he read of in Aristotle, although he mistakenly assumed that Aristotle had approved of it.

Heraclitus (c. 500 B.C.), still another early Greek philosopher whose work, like that of Anaximander and Empedocles, survives only in fragmentary form, also speculated about living things. What views he may have had on the origins of life we don't know, but he felt that conflict was a crucial law governing the relations between living things and that the fittest survived while others became extinguished. It would be risky to read back into Heraclitus anything like our modern notions, by no means clear, of what "survival of the fittest" might mean, or even any evolutionary ideas, however primitive. Nevertheless, to some degree he recognized that the relationships between living things are modified by the struggle between them over the means of survival.

Materialistic and atomistic conceptions of reality, first developed by Democritus, were carried on in antiquity by Epicurus (341–270 B.C.), who exerted great influence on educated Greeks and Romans for generations. Consistent with their strictly materialistic view of the universe, Epicureans postulated that all species had come into being in the remote past, in their present forms, through a process of spontaneous generation. When the earth was young, it possessed the powers of creating life, but now that it had become old, the womb of nature, the earth itself, was sterile. The Roman poet Lucretius (c. 96–55 B.C.) in his magnificent poem *De rerum natura*, "On the Nature of Things," has left us the most complete account of Epicurean doctrine we possess and, in a beautiful passage, he laments the sterile old age of the earth.

The Epicureans, being materialists who tried to explain all phenomena in terms of the physical properties of things and combinations of atoms, followed the lead of Empedocles and gave a thoroughly mechanistic account of the structure as well as the origin of living things. In a famous example, the Epicureans argued that even the most intricate of organs, the eye itself, had come into being by an essentially random conjunction of numerous atoms and that vision followed upon its appearance. Teleological thinkers would have argued that nature "made" the eye in order to express the function of vision, not that the eye was essentially a random product, however complex, and that vision is just what this particular chance configuration of matter is able to do. The eye is certainly an astonishingly engineered organ and it is difficult, though by no means impossible, to think of it as having arisen out of innumerable small variations. The vertebrate eye, for example, is so constructed that most conceivable changes we might want to make in it would simply interfere with its functioning. Even Darwin, convinced as he was of the role of chance variation and natural selection as the motive powers of evolution, had misgivings when he thought of the eye as coming about through this process. Obviously it did, but the eye, from Lucretius down almost to modern times, has been the exemplary organ for battles between mechanists and teleologists.

Of interest to us in all of these early theories is the fact that the men who thought of them were convinced that the living world they saw about them had not always been the same.

Present conditions and present phenomena seemed to point to a different past, to a time when the world was different. Moreover, living things were not, as it were, self-explanatory. They had not always existed, from eternity, just as they are, as Aristotle thought; there had been a time when there was no life at all on earth. In spite of Aristotle's greatness as a biologist, far beyond the general level of these his predecessors, the earlier Greek thinkers we have been considering were in some respects right. The universe, living and nonliving, is at least to some degree the result of a process of change, and from knowledge of the present we may infer what a different past may have been like.

However brilliant these early Greek views on the origin of life may be, it is clear that no Greek thinker conceived of species originating by a process of transformation from simpler to more complex forms of life. Their speculations all took for granted that the species we see about us came into existence in their present forms. Perhaps they were created in a sequence, or they came into being through chance combinations of preexistent parts, or they all arose, small or large, simple or complicated, by spontaneous generation from the primeval earth. No one conjectured, however, that species developed out of one another and that the forms of life were actually related through lines of descent, however divergent.

Some scholars have thought that the Greeks, who had so many marvelous ideas, missed the idea of organic evolution because they did not have any clear notion of how truly ancient the earth was and so could not conceive of a sufficiently long time scale for the slow work of evolutionary change to take place. This, however, does not seem to be true. It is certainly true that after the Christianization of Europe, people believed for centuries that the creation of the universe had occurred only a couple of thousand years before the birth of Christ, but Aristotle and other Greek thinkers had thought the universe was eternal. Had Aristotle needed a sufficiently long time scale for evolution, he would have had all of time to play with. But Aristotle believed that species were as eternal as the universe.

There was no beginning of life as there was no beginning to the cosmos.

There are subtler and more important reasons why evolution and species change seemed impossible to the greatest and most influential biologist of antiquity. On philosophical grounds Aristotle, like his teacher Plato, believed that what is "higher" and more complex must pre-exist the "lower" and less complex. In biological terms this means that the oak, for example, the "goal" of development of the acorn, must in some sense, if only a logical one, pre-exist the acorn. To the question of what comes first, the chicken or the egg, Aristotle would have said neither, in a historical sense: there had always been both chickens and eggs. In a logical sense, however, the chicken is first. To put it in quite crude but perhaps helpful terms, the egg would not know how to develop into a chicken unless chickens already existed. One measure of the distance we have traveled from this view of things is the remark I believe to be attributed to Samuel Butler, the English novelist who was much interested in evolution, that a hen is just the egg's way of making another egg!

Underlying Aristotle's view of development lies a radically different idea of change. In the Greek view of things change was cyclical, never indefinitely progressive. If the complex could not be imagined as arising out of the more simple, it was even less possible to imagine any process of change which would not at some point be a process of decay. The model and limit for all organic change was the life of the individual: one is born, grows to a maximum of development, and then declines into death.

A second reason why Aristotle could not imagine the transformation of species lies in his own biological work. He was, more than almost any other biologist, immensely struck by the adaptedness of living things. To him, an organism was such an integrated whole, its parts so carefully attuned to their function and to each other, that random processes like those of the atomists or Empedocles could not account for its structure. Any significant change in an organism would have been like tampering with a finely made mechanism. Thus, however closely related some organisms were to one another, that resemblance was not the result of common ancestry and divergence through variation, but a reflection of the fixed order of nature.

In the last analysis, Aristotle, like Plato, carried to its conclusion a supposition which underlay most Greek science and philosophy, that knowledge and inquiry would disclose an essentially unchanging order of things. Plato went to great extremes in this view and held that no knowledge could really be had of changing things. For him the only true science was geometry! Aristotle, on the other hand, took brilliant account of different kinds of change within a framework of eternal order. His analysis of development, his accounts of different kinds of physical change, are masterpieces of their kind. But these changes all took place within a framework of unchanging order and were all recurrent, cyclical in character, rather than progressive or linear. What was lacking in Greek thought which is so necessary for the idea of evolution, organic or cosmological, was the conception of continual change in a linear direction, the idea that the universe as a whole is different at one time than at another time, and that the processes of change are in principle and in the long run irreversible.

Whether this linear, irreversible current of change is thought of as "progress" in some sense of the word is not particularly important from the scientific point of view. What is important is that Greek thinkers did not conceive of reality as a continual *process*. An occasional thinker like Heraclitus thought that the world was in continual change, that it was never exactly the same from one moment to the next, and that knowledge could only reside in understanding the laws or principles which governed change. This sounds rather close to our modern view and in some respects it is, but Heraclitus did not think of change as directional, as process. Whatever laws of change men discovered would be laws dealing with eternally recurrent patterns.

The idea of process implies that new things come into the world. Cosmic gases condense to form stars and planets. Galaxies were once much closer together and are now receding from each other. Life appears where there was no life and proliferates into new forms over long periods of time. Stars age and eventually grow cold, while new stars are slowly being made. In short the cosmos, living or nonliving, has a history in some sense analogous to the way in which the human race has a history. Unlike the human historical process in which all events are in some degree significantly unique, the history of the cosmos and of life is governed by regularities; at least the regularities are what interest us. Julius Caesar and the events he dominated will never occur again. This is an important fact to the historian of human affairs. The differences between one grain of sand and another are of little if any scientific interest.

If the regularities of this process are what interest us, how do we discover what principles govern these regularities? The answer is deceptively simple. The laws that govern natural phenomena now are basically the same as those which governed the process of cosmological and organic evolution. At one time, when a scientist thought he had discovered a law of nature, he assumed that he had discovered a principle which ensured that everything had always been the same. The laws of planetary motion, for example, were thought of as eternally true, in the sense that there had always been a solar system for those laws to be exemplified in. Today, the astronomer might say that laws of planetary motion describe the functioning of the solar system at this phase in its long history. There are certainly "laws" or regularities in nature. We can safely assume that oxygen one billion years ago had exactly the same properties it has now. But it existed under different conditions in a different physicochemical system. The laws of nature, the properties of the elements, remain the same, but they operate in a complex system of changing interrelations to bring forth new configurations over long aeons of time.

The ancient, essentially static conception of the physical and organic universe dominated men's minds for centuries, indeed down to the end of the eighteenth century. All of the great contributions to taxonomy and natural history which were the achievement of the modern era down to that time had been inserted into the Aristotelian scheme of things, his timeless hierarchy of life. This scheme, as we have seen, was not simply a convenient and suggestive way of arranging living things, but a way of looking at all of reality, a view shot through with philosophical and religious assumptions. Any biologist today would probably agree that there is a perfectly commonsense way of regarding a sponge as simpler than a horse, or of regarding man as the outcome of one particular line of evolutionary development. But no biologist, speaking strictly as a scientist, would say that a horse is in some mysterious sense better than a sponge or that the whole course of evolution with all of its aeons of time, its "errors" and "waste," has man as a purpose and intention. The horse, the sponge and man are all outcomes of particular lines of evolutionary development. The features of organisms or of the evolutionary process itself which suggest purposefulness in any anthropomorphic sense of the term are the result of adaptation, a property of life which can be quite satisfactorily explained without appeal to unverifiable principles or vitalistic forces. A sponge is perfect at being a sponge, as a horse is best at being a horse. There is no comparison between them in terms of "perfection" or other values of a similar kind.

Not only did classical taxonomy bequeath to biological science a hierarchical scheme of the "tree of life" replete with implicit and explicit assumptions of a philosophical and religious character, but under biblical influence, this tree of life was thought of as having come into existence all at once in an act of divine creation with each species corresponding to an idea or "archetype" in the mind of the Creator. If Aristotle thought species were eternal, pious taxonomists thought they were created all at once. In either case the result was the same: species were fixed and unchanging. Variations from a supposed ideal type, according to either account of the nature of species, were thought of as freaks, aberrations, stubborn failures of matter to embody an ideal form. The grand taxonomic map of life was timeless and unchanging. It had always been what we find it to be and it would never change.

At about the same time that this view of the order of living things reached its ultimate development, largely with the work of Linnaeus, others were beginning to suggest in tentative ways that the grand scheme might not be changeless. The encyclopedic French naturalist Georges de Buffon (1707–1788), who wrote voluminously on natural history, suggested that species—for example the horse—might vary some, but through a kind of degeneration only and strictly within the limits of the "genus"—of "horseness," we might say. Thus, according to Buffon, several varieties of horses were the "degenerate" descendants of the "best" or ideal species of horse. He never suggested that the horse might vary enough over a long period of time to produce an animal which would be quite different, even different enough to constitute a new form of life.

Even though Buffon did not advance evolutionary ideas as such, he had an important influence in propounding a more dynamic view of life. Even if all change in species was degenerative and bounded by the limits of the genus, he did maintain that the local distribution of species might change through the effects of predation or competition for food supply. This may not seem so important from our point of view today, but it marked a radical departure from the static character of biological thinking so characteristic of the eighteenth century. Buffon at least thought that some variation of species was possible, and he did establish a link, unexplained as he left it, between this fact and ecological factors. Along with his more dynamic conceptions, there went the notion of life as contained in a system of altering relations between species, and between them and the environment. His contemporaries were far more concerned with defining what species were and arranging them in a scale. The burning question for many in his time was not how species came into being—they were assumed to be created—but what they were and even whether they "really" existed. These debates remind us of the old medieval debates between nominalists and realists, the former saying that all general class concepts are mere convenient fictions and that only individuals exist, and the others saying that class concepts, like species, are the truly real categories of being and that the individuals merely embody more or less adequately their type.

Erasmus Darwin (1731–1802), the grandfather of the great Charles Darwin, suggested that species may change by reacting to the environment in such ways that they would be permanently modified. Thus a polar bear is an ordinary bear, so to speak, which has been permanently modified by its arctic environment. He also suggested that all warm-blooded animals may have evolved from a "living filament" endowed by God with powers of growth and transformation, and that all living things might have evolved from spontaneously generated microorganisms. Although Erasmus Darwin appears to have recognized that changes in species were adaptive, he could offer no explanation of how such changes actually came about. He was far from suggesting anything like the comprehensive evolutionary ideas which were the work of his grandson.

Such tentative approaches to evolutionary theory may strike us as quite timid, and more than one historian has suggested that Buffon, at any rate, was inhibited by fear of offending ecclesiastical authorities or religious sensibilities. In fact, it is much more likely that the great impediments to the development of ideas concerning organic evolution lay more in the pervasive influence of certain traditional habits of thought than in anything else. The great and influential tradition of philosophical thought we have already encountered in Aristotle assumed that more complex realities could not arise from simpler ones, or something perfect from something less perfect. Things might decay or degenerate, break up into simpler units, after they had reached their limit of individual development, but the reverse could not take place. Clearly, Buffon's notion of limited and strictly degenerative species change is a direct deduction from such a view.

Even those who did entertain more radical evolutionary ideas, like Erasmus Darwin, lacked any conception of a *mechanism* by which the evolutionary process might work. Beyond these difficulties, prevailing ideas on the chronology of the earth allowed very little time for the gradual and scarcely visible changes which evolutionary theory required. It was abundantly clear to all that if evolution indeed occurred, it would have to be an extremely gradual process. After all, to use a famous example we shall soon turn to, no one had ever seen an antelope turn into a giraffe! Orthodoxy, which allowed only six thousand years to the total history of the world, past, present and future, left far too little time for species to change in.

In the history of thought, it frequently happens that a good idea is suggested prematurely, at a time when supporting ancillary ideas are lacking, or when other ideas, held to be true, impede the acceptance of the new one. We have seen one example in Buffon's notion of limited species change through degeneration. An earlier example can be found in the series of discoveries which led up to Harvey's discovery of the circulation of the blood. Evidence which Harvey used to show that the blood circulates had previously been used to support the Galenical theory of venous ebb and flow simply because enough evidence had not yet accumulated to offer any plausible alternative to Galen. It was scientifically sensible for Servetus to use his discovery of the pulmonary circulation to try to save the one coherent theory of circulation then available.

It cannot be emphasized too much that ideas do not exist as isolated entities but in a complex network of interrelations. As technology and practical human needs have profoundly altered the course of scientific research and often determined the subjects of major scientific effort, so the state of one branch of knowledge may profoundly influence the progress of another branch. We have already encountered examples of the relations between advances in chemistry and physics and advances in biology. A more remote example from the history of astronomy may be useful in illustrating this point even further. The earth-centered Ptolemaic solar system became the standard astronomical system of antiquity and remained so until Copernicus set forth his theories in the sixteenth century. Now ancient astronomers and mathematicians realized that it was quite possible to explain all of the movements of the heavenly bodies in terms of a heliocentric theory of the solar system. There was more than one system of astronomy which would, as they put it, "save the appearances." Moreover, it was realized that there might be some advantages to arranging the universe otherwise than the arrangement of Ptolemy. Why then did the geocentric theory prevail? The answer lies more in the nature of ancient physics than in ancient astronomy. Ancient physicists postulated four elements, earth, air, fire and water. Each of these had a "natural place," that is, fire always went up and earth always down to the center of the cosmos. If the sun was made of fire and fire went up, how could it be assumed to be at the center of the cosmos? The heliocentric theory would have meant throwing out the whole system of ancient physics and, moreover, with nothing to replace it. However wrong that physics may seem to us now, we must understand that the same desire to comprehend the workings of things which leads men to investigate them also leads men to cling to whatever explanations they have, even if these are inadequate. Men desire to know not simply how one particular aspect of reality works, but how their knowledge of particulars fits into some larger system of explanations.

We have covered enough of the history of biology at this point to understand the development of scientific theories like evolution in the light of these illustrations and principles. The historian cannot ever indulge in the rather arrogant luxury of hindsight and look at the history of science as if it were a conflict between the wise and the ignorant, intellectual cowboys and Indians, so to speak. There has some times been truth on the "wrong" side of a question; discoveries which seem simple to us required a long time for their appearance and, often, the mightiest efforts of the best intellects. The past might well have been different. As Sir Isaac Newton said, "If we see further, it is because we stand on the shoulders of giants."

The first man to work out a theory of organic evolution in any systematic and detailed way, and to suggest a mechanism for the process as well, was Jean Baptiste de Lamarck (1744–1829). Lamarck has often been pretty roughly handled by historians of science and culture, partly because he was such a poor writer and partly because of the extravagance of some of his ideas, but he must, in all fairness, be given credit as an important figure in the history of biological thought. He was, in the first place, an excellent taxonomist and made an exhaustive study of invertebrates, the best up to his time. He anticipated the development of cell theory and was probably the first to use the term "biology" to cover all of the life sciences.

Lamarck thus came to the speculative side of biology with considerable preparation in detailed biological observation. It was doubtless his long experience with the invertebrates which led him to speculate on the possibility of the more complex forms of life being derived from the simpler. After all, some ninety percent of animal species belong to this rather unsatisfactory category we have set up for them, and their variety of forms and modes of existence are far richer in suggestions of possible evolutionary relationships than anything which obtains among the vertebrates.

Lamarck's view of evolution was in many respects an odd one. For one thing, he believed that all of the microscopic forms of life such as the protozoa were continually arising out of inorganic matter through spontaneous generation. The more complex forms of life not only had derived from these simple forms but were continuing to do so, although the process was so slow that it was not really detectable. In short, Lamarck thought that all organisms were evolving toward man and, after long stretches of time, would *become* man. There are not, in this view, different lines of evolution leading in different directions. On the contrary, life emerges spontaneously in its simplest forms and, so to speak, climbs the taxonomic ladder toward man at the top. Even for the state of biological and philosophical knowledge of the time, this view is rather fanciful and was subjected to severe criticism by those who also might have been willing to entertain evolutionary ideas.

The most stringent criticism of Lamarck's views, however, was directed at his account of the mechanism of evolution. Lamarck believed in the inheritance of acquired characteristics.

This, in itself, was not necessarily an idea to arouse the contempt of scientists. Darwin himself found the idea plausible and allowed for the inheritance of acquired characteristics in his theory of heredity. What seemed absurd was Lamarck's notion that organisms somehow "willed" a good many of the modifications they acquired and passed on to their progeny. Quite what Lamarck meant by his idea of "will" is obscure. He seems to have meant that organisms strive to accomplish certain necessary tasks, modify their structures in so doing, and transmit that modification to their progeny. This seems to be the meaning of Lamarck's famous example of how the giraffe, a newly discovered animal at that time, might have evolved from the antelope.

Lamarck assumed, on the basis of some substantial evidence, that an organ will grow in size if it is used and will degenerate if there is no need for it. He further assumed, however, that changes of this sort occurring in the lifetime of an individual would be passed on to its descendants. The antelope whose descendants eventually turned into giraffes found itself in an environment where it had to dine off the leaves of trees. Changes in climate or other physical conditions had eliminated or distinctly reduced the grass it habitually grazed on. As it sought more to eat it had to stretch its neck and its whole body, including its legs. The ensuing development of the exercised body parts, however slight in one generation, would be passed on to the offspring of the antelope in question who, in turn, would go through the same performance. In time, through the sum of small incremental changes, you would have a giraffe.

This example of Lamarck's became a joke among biologists for decades. There was and still is no evidence that this is the way species change. Yet the idea, from the historical point of view, should not be dismissed out of hand. Lamarck did postulate an *intelligible,* if unsound, mechanism for organic evolution and the variation of species. If it is true, as it is, that there is no worthwhile evidence that acquired characteristics are inherited, Lamarck at least has the merit of suggesting some specific way in which species might change. Far more serious was the failure of Lamarck's mechanism to account for other important adaptive phenomena. If it is, however remotely, conceivable that through striving, or a kind of willing, an organism adapts itself to a different environment through the use or disuse of body parts which then become so modified as to eventually create a new species, how does one account for the adaptation of plants? Or insects, even? Does an insect with protective coloration practice changing the color of its external covering? Does the bee, through some sort of voluntary effort, practice creating the complex architectural and social structure of the hive?

The book in which Lamarck exponded these theories, *Philosophie zoologique* (1890), has finally come to be treated as a scientific curiosity. Nevertheless, Lamarck effectively placed a bold version of organic evolution in the marketplace of scientific ideas and, for this if for nothing else, he deserves some gratitude from posterity. Stripped of its more fanciful side, his theory exerted considerable influence on some biologists for a long time, and his four laws which were presumed to govern the evolutionary process remained a part of the climate of evolutionary thought until evolution was given a new foundation in modern genetics. These laws were the following:

1. A living individual increases in size to a predetermined limit.
2. New organs are produced over a long period of time *in response to a need.*
3. An organ develops in size and efficiency to the extent that it is used and atrophies to the extent that it is not used.
4. All the traits acquired by an individual are transmitted to its offspring.

Lamarck's views, in some respects, had been anticipated by Erasmus Darwin, who also believed that acquired characteristics could be inherited and that these would cause far-reaching changes in animals. Lamarck, however, thought that the main mechanism of change was organ use and disuse while Erasmus Darwin had assumed a direct influence of the environment on the organism. In the light of our modern notions of evolution, both these men assumed a mechanism of evolutionary change which controlled mutations. That is, either the environment in a general way or the creature's activity in an environment directly affected the hereditary material. Whatever changes were so produced entered directly into the genotype, or hereditary constitution of the organism. The main trouble with this view is that there is no evidence at all that this can occur, and it seems less and less likely as our knowledge of genetics grows.

Neo-Lamarckians have turned up in the history of modern biology fairly regularly, if not in large numbers. Stripped of its more fanciful aspects, Lamarckianism, or the notion that acquired characteristics can be hereditary, is hard to refute, in spite of the fact that there is no convincing evidence for it. Direct observation won't help much. After all, it takes immense periods of time for a species to change in any really conspicuous way, and it is also difficult to conceive of experimental conditions for testing Lamarck's theory. In order to be sure that the changes in a population, for example, were purely the result of members of that population having transmitted *acquired* characteristics to their offspring, we would have to start the experiment with genetically pure lines of the organism we select. This is quite difficult to do. Even if we could, and the results of our experiment were negative for Lamarck, his disciples could always reply that we had not conducted our experiment for a long enough time.

Furthermore, it would be extremely difficult to place any population of organisms in such conditions that we could be certain that the only factors modifying them would be environmental. How could we eliminate the influence of selective processes? After all, any environment is bound to have a selective effect on a population, favoring some individuals over others, in however slight a degree. Even Lamarckians must agree that any population will have some range of variety in it for selection to work on. The most telling objection to Lamarckianism, however, is furnished by the great amounts of data we now possess on the rate of evolution. If organisms do inherit acquired characteristics they must do so at so slow a rate—if they did so rapidly and in large numbers we could detect them—that a Lamarckian view of the evolutionary process will simply not account for the known rate of evolutionary change. It is interesting that a Lamarckian account of the evolution of life would require more time than was actually needed, for many of the objections to evolutionary ideas, whether Lamarck's or Darwin's, were based on the conviction that the earth was simply not old enough for evolution to have been possible. Such arguments were by no means advanced only by religious fundamentalists but, as we shall see, by geologists and physicists who, even if uninfluenced by biblical chronology, thought that the evidence in their possession did not point to the many millions of years evolution required.

The important new ideas which would change the intellectual climate sufficiently to prepare for the great work of Darwin came not from biology but from astronomy and geology. In 1755 Immanuel Kant, the great philosopher, advanced the notion that the solar system had not always been the way we find it but that it had been formed out of a vast contracting or condensing nebula. In short, it had evolved to its present state from a state which was quite different. Kant's hypothesis was the work of pure and brilliant speculation. Some forty years later, in 1796, the nebular hypothesis of the formation of the solar system was placed on a mathematical and physical basis by the French astronomer Laplace. The English astronomer William Herschel, not long after, on the basis of painstaking observation of the heavens, postulated that stars as well as the solar system were derived by condensation or contraction of nebulae.

These three remarkable men established that the physical universe was not a great changeless mechanism, much like an immense clock, but that it had come to be what it now is through a process of change. Moreover, the same changes were still slowly occurring. Both the observational and the indirect evidence adduced to support this new cosmology were compelling enough to constitute a major breach in the intellectual time barrier. The cosmos had a history and it was clearly a long one.

Detectable changes in the order of the heavens proceeded at a very slow rate, and it must have taken millennia for the stars and our solar system to have been formed out of the nebulous gases from which they originated. Scientific study of the present state of things had shown that we could not account for the way things are now without assuming that they were quite different in a remote past. As the astronomers of the sixteenth and seventeenth centuries, Galileo, Tycho Brahe, Kepler and Newton, had vastly extended our notion of the distances of cosmic space, the astronomers of this later period were pushing back the dimension of time to an equally great degree.

The first great change in geological theories came with the work of James Hutton (1726–1797), a medical man by profession but an enthusiastic student of geology. In 1785 he published his *Theory of the Earth* in which he advanced his theory of geological change. Hutton noted, as indeed had others before him, that wind and rain, heat and cold, the flowing of water and other such physical conditions shaped and modified the earth's surface. He maintained, however, that these forces not only were the essential molders of the earth but that they always had been. Moreover, they had always operated in much the same way and to the same effect as they do now. The geological history of the earth was therefore uniform, insofar as the types of forces and their manner of acting were concerned. This view of geological change came to be called "uniformitarianism" and was later opposed, as we shall see, to "catastrophism," or the notion that the earth was shaped essentially by periodic dramatic upheavals.

One important consequence flowed from Hutton's work. If the geological forces he postulated had always acted as slowly as they do now, then it must have taken a tremendously long time for these forces to make mountains, carve out rivers, wear away great boulders and change the contours of the continents.

Later in the eighteenth century, a young Englishman, William Smith (1769–1839), discovered that the series of animal fossils succeeded each other in a regular order. He was by profession neither a geologist nor a biologist but a surveyor, engaged in laying out the routes of networks of canals then widely under construction in England. As he watched the excavations, he noted that certain groups of fossil species were always to be found under other distinct groups. Each stratum of rock, no matter how convoluted or how various the different levels it assumed over a large area, always had the same fossil species. Indeed, Smith was the first man to identify the type of rock by its fossil content alone. Fossils had long been observed but few guessed how old they really were. Leonardo da Vinci, an acute observer, had noticed marine fossils in the countryside around Florence and conjectured that a long time ago the land he stood on must have been under the ocean. Others, less original, thought that the fossils might be left over from the biblical Flood, which was presumed to have happened only a few thousand years before. Whatever the theories about them, fossils received no extensive systematic study until the work of Georges Cuvier (1769–1832).

Cuvier was a truly remarkable anatomist and placed anatomy on a solidly comparative basis. His wide-ranging comparative studies gave him a profound understanding of the nature of different animal body plans, an understanding so deep and coordinated that he was able to reconstruct an entire animal from a few crucial parts. He gave extensive accounts of how, for example, the structure of certain bones will imply the structure of the whole skeleton of which they are a part and even give clues to the kind of tissues which must have been associated with them. On the basis of these studies, he expanded and improved the Linnaean system of classification by discovering closer affinities between groups of organisms than Linnaeus had realized existed. He introduced the term "phylum" to cover these newly unified groups of organisms. Even his minor modifications of Linnaean taxonomy reflect a far deeper understanding of biological structure.

Cuvier, in fact, made the most brilliant use after Aristotle of the principle of the correlation of parts. In his taxonomical work, he had made a fourfold classification of the metazoa according to completely diverse body plans and systems of correlated body parts. They were *vertebrata,* the vertebrates, *articulata,* "jointed" animals like crayfish or spiders, *mollusca,* snails and the like, and *radiata,* all organisms that did not fit the other three categories and which were presumed to possess a radial body plan, like the starfish, for example.

Within these four types of body plan, Cuvier showed a common principle at work. The shape of every organ and structure is determined by its function, and these functional structures are in turn correlated to each other by the way an animal performs the activities necessary for life. Thus, an animal with the teeth of a predator must have the right kind of limbs and claws for capturing and holding its prey. A particular kind of feather in a bird will be correlated to a particular kind of structure in the forelimb, the collarbone, the breastbone, all minutely correlated to each other if the bird is to fly.

Thus, when Cuvier turned his attention to fossils he was supremely equipped to make sense of them. The same understanding which enabled him to construct a living animal from its parts led him to construct extinct animals from their few remaining fragments. Not only could he conjecture what the whole of these vanished animals must have been like; he was able to show that they could be classified with groups of animals that were not extinct. With Cuvier paleontology came into being, and his methods and procedures are still the basis of that science. One might imagine, with the work of Hutton in vastly extending the age of the earth and the work of Smith in showing how the fossil record was connected with strata of rock laid down in different times, that Cuvier might have inferred the evolution of species. In fact he did not, and so great was his prestige and that of his tradition that it delayed the acceptance of evolutionary ideas in France when they finally were convincingly developed.

Nevertheless, Cuvier was too thoughtful a man not to account for the fossil record. He took the view, then current in some geological quarters, that the earth had been shaped by great periodic upheavals. To be sure it was much older than people had thought, but its history had been marked by great catastrophes in which most forms of life had been wiped out. The fossil record is the record of these catastrophes. After each upheaval, the earth was repeopled by the species that remained. Cuvier, a firm believer in the fixity of species, did not postulate successive creations. There was only one such act, and all species of living things, whether now extinct or not, originated at the same time. The catastropes had simply reduced the number of species to the surviving ones. What did Cuvier make of the fact that the fossil record seemed to show the emergence of new species in higher strata? He simply denied that the species were really new and maintained that they must have emigrated after a catastrophe from some other part of the world. He was convinced that a thorough geological study of other regions of the world would show that those fossils which indicate new species in Europe would be found in lower levels of rock elsewhere, in those places from which he presumed they originated.

Cuvier believed that four great catastrophes were all that were needed to account for the fossil record and claimed that in the biblical account of the flood we have, in primitive form, a record of the last of these great upheavals. It was clear that Cuvier's theory allowed no possibility for the existence of a fossil man in the sense of a species of man now extinct. Man, always the same, was one of the creatures to survive the sequence of catastrophes.

Cuvier's great work in paleontology was carried on by an English biologist and anatomist, Richard Owen (1804–1892). It was Owen who reconstructed archaeopteryx, the famous fossil bird so like a reptile in many respects, from very little evidence. In fact, he first inferred the existence of such a creature from the fossil impression of a single feather. Like Cuvier, Owen was a firm believer in the fixity of species and an opponent of evolutionary thought. To us, who visit the great displays of fossils in our museums, paleontology seems to be synonymous with evolution. It is startling to think that two of the very greatest paleontologists were stout opponents of evolution, at the same time that they furnished much of the evidence for what detailed knowledge we possess of the evolutionary history of life on earth.

Cuvier's authority, his power and prestige, crushed the reputation of Lamarck. In fact, it was Cuvier who seized the example of the giraffe and ridiculed Lamarck so effectively that his reputation never recovered. Authority in science, as in other activities of man, sometimes works damage. Yet the role of authority in science—despite the many who find authority a dirty word—has often been of benefit. The authority and prestige of a great scientist or scholar can channel the energies of other men into the solution of a crucial problem. Fashions in scientific study—what problems are thought worthy of investigation—depend not only on intellectual matters and, frequently enough, on practical needs, but also on the authority of some great figure whose bold ideas or brilliant achievements may set the course of scientific inquiry. Authority is, after all, a real attribute of certain individuals, whether it is conferred by law or by achievement. What we should ask is not that authority cease to exist but that it not be beyond question and that it give a rational account of itself. By these standards, Cuvier did not refute Lamarck's arguments in an entirely appropriate way, but drew to some degree upon his greater literary skill and, certainly, upon his far greater prestige.

With the work of Cuvier biology and geology came to possess a common set of problems. The quarrels of geological "uniformitarians" and "catastrophists" became quarrels over biological problems as well. The nature of the fossil record, the nature of the history of life itself, hung upon the interpretation of the geological history of the earth. Thus it was that the greatest single intellectual influence on Darwin was the work of a contemporary geologist, Sir Charles Lyell (1797–1875). Lyell was a uniformitarian and further developed the work of Hutton. He showed that all of the discontinuities in the geological record were of a local nature; that if you studied the geological record over a wide enough area of the earth's surface, you would find ample evidence that there were none of those enormous breaks which the theory of catastrophes demanded. For the earth as a whole there was no evidence that the changes it had undergone were anything other than gradual and continuous. Given enough time—and Lyell stressed this point—all features of the earth from the highest mountains to the ocean floor could be explained by uniformitarian principles. When Darwin embarked on the *Beagle* for his long journey of exploration as the ship's naturalist, he took aboard the first volume of Lyell's *Principles of Geology* (1830). The second volume was sent to him, and he received it in 1832. This was the work which shattered Darwin's creationist beliefs for good and all, disclosed the immense stretches of time which lay in the earth's past, and doubtless implanted the idea in his mind that, given enough time, a gradual series of small changes might lead to spectacular transformations.

Our brief review of some of Darwin's forerunners—or of some, like Cuvier, opposed to evolution yet creating impressive evidence for evolutionists to use—shows us that the question of evolution was far less frequently raised than the question concerning the origin of life and its varieties. We have seen too that it was not until Lamarck that the possibility of evolution through a process of progression, from simple to complex, and of transformation from earlier to later species was first raised in extensive, unequivocal fashion. The traces of biological progressivism or transformation to be found earlier are too tentative to be considered as carrying any great weight. In biological terms, there are analogies to Lamarck before him but no real homologies in evolutionary ideas. To be sure, his mechanism for evolution was unusable, but he first attempted to show, on a comprehensive scale, that the evidence of present-day biological science could be used to infer a differing past condition. While this seems commonplace to us, we must recall how long it took to arrive at this view and what cultural changes of great magnitude had to take place. Back of this attempt to read the history of life was the development of modern methods of historical research from the sixteenth to the eighteenth century. Buffon himself claimed that one could argue about past conditions of life in much the same way that a historian using documents and archives can argue back to what must have happened in human history. If one believes the biological past was a historical process in some sense analogous to the process of human history, one will look at the present state of things with a different eye, searching for those clues in the present operations of things from which one might infer what a different past was like. It could no longer be assumed that the biological past was identical to the present or different from it only in superficial ways.

Charles Darwin (1809–1882) was the greatest naturalist and biological thinker after Aristotle. His extraordinary powers of observation, his gift for systematizing, interpreting and expounding masses of data, his scrupulous intellectual honesty, stamp his work with the sign of genius of the highest order. It is fashionable among some historians of thought to show how much of Darwin's work derived from the work of others and how many of his ideas, taken in isolation to be sure, had been thought of by others, as if greatness in science were simply a matter of having a brainstorm or uncovering a nice new fact. The same sort of charge has been leveled at Newton, at Freud and at other great minds. What gives all of these men their greatness is the fact that they were able to unify all the scattered ideas and data of their predecessors, pull them together in a coherent whole, and plumb the ideas they dealt with and their implications to the depths. In doing this they succeeded in being extraordinarily original, an originality which is the product of a synthetic faculty, of the capacity to bring a lot of material together in a *freshly intelligible way.* It is true that progressivism and transformationism had been thought of before, but Darwin, in his concept of natural selection, found a mechanism for evolution which unified a whole mass of both new and old data, and which proved to be the most useful, illuminating and powerful biological idea of modern times. In short, it has been said of the greatest investigators that they can look at what everyone else sees but think what nobody else could think. We might add that they can even take the thoughts of others, rethink them, and show them to us in an entirely new light.

Darwin's family had destined him for the study of medicine,

but the terrible conditions in the hospitals, where medicine was taught, revolted him and he turned away from it. He thought briefly of entering the ministry, but he soon realized he had no vocation for that either. While at Cambridge he cultivated the study of natural history and soon came to think of it as a possible vocation. In 1831, when Darwin was only twenty-two years old, he accepted the post of naturalist on the *H.M.S. Beagle,* a ship sent out by the British navy on a journey of scientific exploration.

During the eighteenth and nineteenth centuries several great voyages of scientific exploration took place. Every schoolboy has heard of Captain Cook and his famous travels, and any naturalist knows of the voyage of the *Challenger* (1872–1876), perhaps the most ambitious scientific voyage ever undertaken, one whose reports took years to compile and comprise fifty large volumes. But the voyage of the *Beagle* occupies a special place in the history of biology. Less glamorous than the voyages of Cook and less ambitious than that of the *Challenger*, it was the school of the greatest modern biologist.

Darwin was a poor sailor but he bravely put up with seasickness and was away from home for five long years. The results of that journey are recorded in his delightful book *The Voyage of the Beagle.* On this voyage he learned the major lessons, unforgettable ones, which finally issued into *The Origin of Species* (1859). In Darwin's own words, taken from his autobiography, he tells us what they were:

> During the voyage of the *Beagle* I had been deeply impressed by discovering in the Pampean formation [in South America] great fossil animals covered with armour like that on the existing armadillos; secondly, by the manner in which closely allied animals replace one another in proceeding southwards over the Continent; and thirdly, by the South American character of most of the productions of the Galapagos archipelago, and more especially by the manner in which they differ slightly on each island of the group; none of these islands appearing to be very ancient in a geological sense.
>
> It was evident that such facts as these, as well as many

> others, could be explained on the supposition that species gradually became modified; and the subject haunted me. But it was equally evident that neither the action of the surrounding conditions, nor the will of the organisms (especially in the case of plants), could account for the innumerable cases in which organisms of every kind are beautifully adapted to their habits of life,—for instance, a woodpecker or tree-frog to climb trees, or a seed for dispersal by hooks or plumes. I had always been much struck by such adaptations, and until these could be explained it seemed to me almost useless to endeavour to prove by indirect evidence that species have been modified.*

The most remarkable and telling of the observations Darwin made were of the varieties of finches dwelling in the Galápagos Islands, which lie some 650 miles off the coast of Ecuador. Darwin noted that there were some fourteen different species of these finches on the islands and that they were quite unlike their nearest relatives on the mainland. Darwin surmised that the finches on the islands were the descendants of finches who had come there from the mainland a very long time before, and that through small variations occurring over this long period of time, variations like those he noticed on his journey down the coast, the finches he found had come into being. Each of the species, moreover, was marked by a variation of great adaptative significance. The finches varied not only in size and general body plan but most noticeably in their differing beaks, each adapted to a different feeding habit. Some beaks were shaped to get at seeds of one kind or another, others to get at insects, and one remarkable bird, a species which had evolved the long beak but not the long tongue of the woodpecker, ate by picking up twigs or cactus spines and poking out the insects from pieces of bark. Darwin also noted that many more different kinds of birds were to be found on the mainland than in the islands and surmised that the original colony of finches to come to the Galápagos from the mainland must have found very little competition from other birds.

* *The Autobiography of Charles Darwin, 1809–1882,* ed. Nora Barlow (Harcourt, Brace & Company, Inc., 1959), pp. 118–19.

At the time of his observations Darwin could offer no explanation of these small variations in the species of finches. Identical physical conditions had produced a great variety of species, so that the effect of environment had to be discounted. How could species so close together in location be at all different while others so far apart were so similar? After all, the mainland finches were different from the island finches but they were clearly all finches. The sort of explanation his grandfather might have given was thus clearly excluded. Moreover, the "need," or as Lamarck might have said, the "will," of the organism would not explain anything either. Even if an antelope might stretch its neck through practice, it is pretty hard to think of a bird as stretching or reshaping its beak, and as Darwin very astutely pointed out in the passage we quoted, plants are as beautifully adapted as animals and it is simply inconceivable to think of any process like a Lamarckian one as accounting for these variations.

Then, a couple of years after his return from the voyage of the *Beagle*, Darwin came across a remarkable book by a man who belongs perhaps more to the history of economics than to that of biology. This book, *An Essay on the Principle of Population*, by the Reverend Thomas Malthus (1766–1834), first appeared before Darwin was born, in 1798, and years later it gave Darwin a clue to the answer he needed. Malthus had argued that in any country the food supply of the population would increase in an arithmetic series while the population would double itself much faster, in a geometric series. A population would double itself much faster, therefore, than food supply could conceivably be doubled. Population, therefore, had to be held in check. Famine, disease and war were the agencies by which this had been accomplished in the past, but Malthus noted that, at least in his part of the world, such "natural" checks were for obvious reasons becoming less effective. He warned that unless populations were restricted through some voluntary means, the future of mankind would be very bleak indeed.

Darwin was struck by Malthus' argument and immediately

inferred that if it was true for human life it was true for other forms of life as well. There was thus a struggle for existence among various forms of life and competition for survival. As such, this idea had been stated before, by Buffon, and even by the ancient Greek thinker Heraclitus. How then did Darwin make fresh use of this idea?

Darwin was a countryman and lived in close touch with farm people. It had long been common practice for farmers to mate their livestock to improve the breed. New kinds of horses and cattle had been deliberately created by careful interbreeding so as to emphasize some feature or other that was desirable. This was artificial selection, and Darwin had himself bred pigeons to study the possible consequences of different kinds of matings. Moreover, this man on whom no observation was lost had noted, as we all do, that in any group of offspring, a litter of kittens, say, there will be variations. Some will be larger, some livelier, some of different color. Now if species are continually varying in small ways, it is conceivable that some of these variations will be advantageous in the struggle for existence that Malthus had postulated. A larger breed of animal might have an advantage over its smaller related breeds in defending itself from enemies or in getting the food it needs. The smaller, weaker strains then might simply die out. By their sheer capacity to survive, the stronger breeds would have a reproductive advantage over their less well fitted cousins and would in the course of time replace them.

This was somewhat like the process by which a farmer picks certain animals to breed and prohibits others from doing so in order to improve his stock. Obviously nature is not a conscious selecting agency. Yet the natural process seemed analogous enough to the artificial one for Darwin to coin the phrase "natural selection." It is important to stress this analogy, because some accounts of Darwin refer to the "survival of the fittest" without calling our attention to what was clearly in Darwin's mind when he thought of natural selection. The fittest were not only those who survived the contest, as it were, but those who survived it in such a way that they possessed a *reproductive advantage* over their weaker brethren. They were "selected" to reproduce. They had not only to survive but to be able to make more of themselves and pass on their advantageous characteristics to their offspring. The latter would then enter the world as well equipped for the struggle as their parents.

Applied to the finches, this conception of evolution might work as follows: the first finches to reach the Galápagos Islands were seed-eating birds. There were few if any other species of birds on the islands, but lots of seeds. With no competition, no predators and lots of food, the finches multiplied abundantly. At a certain point, however, Malthus' inexorable law came into effect. The weaker or smaller finches starved while the stronger and swifter survived. Now in any breeding population there will be some variation. Let us suppose that among these variations there is a finch with a somewhat differently constructed beak, a beak that will permit it to pick out an insect from the bark of the tree. It may not like insects, but if that is the only thing it can eat it might try it to avoid starvation. It is thus able to use a new food source. It survives and breeds, even if it is in some respects weaker and smaller than those finches able to compete successfully for the limited supply of seeds in the now crowded habitat. If it transmits this special kind of beak to its young, they will have the advantage of being able to use a new food source and will be favored in the struggle for existence by that fact. That advantage will translate itself into reproductive advantage by the very fact that they can survive to maturity. They will not be held in check by starvation as the seed-eating finches will be at the time, although they too will someday come up against the Malthusian principle. The environment thus favors some of the differences produced by the natural process of small variations over others. This process is not purposive. It is strictly automatic. Life varies and the environment, so to speak, acts on those differences. Those variations which are advantageous and inheritable will favor the survival of one variety over another.

So far this is clear enough and not at all implausible or

difficult to believe. Quite similar results had been produced by pigeon fanciers, for example. Now Darwin made a great leap of the imagination. Assuming, as he had to, that variations simply occur and without being able to explain the mechanism of variation itself, he went through something like the following chain of argument: if *inheritable* variations occurred often enough, and if at least some of these varying individuals lived in an environment in which their particular variation conferred on them a *reproductive* advantage (from the point of view of evolution there is no point in being terribly fit for the struggle for existence if you are sterile or if your advantages in this respect are not transmitted to sufficient offspring), then the ideas of Malthus would explain the remarkable adaptations of those animals who survive the great struggle.

Darwin also postulated that the properties of varying individuals should not be overwhelmed by the consequences of crossbreeding. In other words, circumstances should be such that reproduction went on between the more favored types. This last point was extremely important, and further knowledge since Darwin's time has tended to modify his assumptions about the conditions necessary to make it probable that variations will not be nullified by interbreeding. He believed, as did his successors in the study of evolution down to more recent times, that species evolved by adaptation to differing circumstances in the *same* area. Extensive studies since that time have given little evidence that such is the case. Geographical isolation seems to be necessary for the production of new species, and it would seem to be the only method by which new species of birds arise. This does not invalidate Darwin's argument about natural selection, however. The different kinds of finches developed among the islands in geographical isolation and then spread out, after speciation, to take up existence and live side by side in varying combinations. In fact, whatever species are found together on one or another of the islands, they are sufficiently differentiated to avoid interbreeding (the Galápagos finches recognize members of the same species for mating purposes by the shape of the beak) and sufficiently differentiated in food habits not to compete for the same sources (different species of finches eat large, medium or small seeds, while others eat insects).

According to Darwin, if this process of random variation and natural selection went on long enough, in terms for example of the great stretches of time that Lyell had been convinced lay behind the earth, then it was conceivable that variants deriving from the same ancestral stock might eventually come to differ so widely from one another that they would appear to be utterly unrelated creatures. Given sufficient time, continual variation, however small and random, the action of physical environmental factors such as climate and of biological environmental factors such as food supply or predators, we can account for the origin of all existing species.

Darwin did not "prove" evolution of species. He simply gathered so much evidence, related it to so much that was known of geology, paleontology, zoology, botany and animal husbandry, that he left his readers with no other *intelligible* alternative. Moreover, he described a mechanism for evolution which not only made the facts intelligible but which, in an analogous way, was observable in the artificial selection man had been practicing for so long, as well as in nature itself.

Darwin was such a painstaking and encyclopedic worker that he almost delayed the publication of his views too long. Alfred Wallace (1823–1913), another English naturalist, had come to quite similar conclusions to those of Darwin and sent the manuscript of a paper setting them forth to Darwin for comment, not knowing that Darwin had long been thinking similar thoughts. Darwin was amazed at the coincidence and communicated it to Lyell, who arranged to have both Darwin's work and that of Wallace presented together in 1858. Darwin rushed his great work to completion and published *The Origin of Species* one year later. Darwin had worked slowly because he knew that his theory could carry conviction only if it explained the widest possible array of facts. Hence he collected widely varied data: on the so-called "vestigial" organs of existing species, like the bone structures in the flippers of whales which show that they must have once been legs; on protective coloration; on the sexual selection so conspicuous in some species of birds, in which the most gorgeously plumed male has a better chance with the ladies. The more he could bring together and explain, the more he could persuade his readers.

We might mention in passing that Wallace and Darwin never entered those absurd and sometimes disgraceful controversies over priority which mark the history of science. All scientific work goes on in a community of knowledge, and it does not detract one iota from Darwin's greatness to say that the time was ripe for his contribution. More than once in the history of science we have instances of simultaneous discovery. It is an unhappy fact that the discovery of the calculus by both Newton and Leibnitz quite independently of each other led to a good deal of acrimony.

Darwin's book in its full title was called *On the Origin of Species by Means of Natural Selection, or the Preservation of Favoured Races in the Struggle for Life,* a complete statement of its thesis and striking title. A first small printing was sold out the very day it appeared, and the book subsequently went through innumerable printings. Considering that Darwin had had his manuscript turned down by several different publishers, *The Origin of Species* was one of the greatest "sleepers" in the history of publishing as well as what has been called the single most important book in the history of scientific thought. It placed biology on a sound basis by providing a theoretical framework of great utility and illuminating power for the widest array of facts. Beyond this, it had an enormous impact on other branches of learning and on the general culture of modern times. It was enthusiastically received in some quarters and violently attacked in others. Some of the most vocal opposition came from religious leaders who objected to the exclusively naturalistic account that Darwin gave of the origin of species. God did not seem to be a necessary hypothesis for Darwin in accounting for the origin of the universe and of life. Others, less orthodox perhaps but committed to certain philosophical and quasi-religious views, were repelled by the Darwinian vision of the blind operations of natural selection on random variation. There seemed to be no purpose to the whole process that Darwin described, and in the eyes of these critics, he reduced life to a meaningless spectacle of struggle and survival. Others like Richard Owen, the great English paleontologist and disciple of Cuvier, objected somewhat less to the idea of evolution than to the notion of chance variation leading to adaptation. Like Cuvier, and indeed like Darwin himself, Owen was struck by the marvelous adaptive structures of living things; so struck, however, that he could not conceive of their being the outcome of processes involving chance. He maintained that, if species had evolved at all, they must have done so through the power of some inner principle of purposefulness, some power which shaped them according to an immanent design. Such an idea of course explains nothing at all, but it was more satisfactory from an emotional point of view.

Evolutionary theories were adapted to other disciplines, and Herbert Spencer (1820–1903) applied the concept of evolution and that of the struggle for existence to the development of human societies. Unfortunately, the rather simple-minded application of Darwinian notions to society led him to propose that the "unfit," presumably the unemployable or the helpless, should really be left alone to be "selected out," i.e. die, and that assistance to them ran counter to the proper course of evolutionary progress. Some of these notions came to be applied by militarists to the glorification of war as a struggle which decided who was most fit to rule. Obviously, such distortions are based on a misunderstanding of both the range and the limits of Darwin's ideas and of the nature of human society. Civilization is based not simply on competition but to an even greater degree on cooperation. Even in the animal world, wherever we find anything approaching social organization, cooperative principles are at work. Moreover, it is exceedingly hard to determine who is fit to survive in human society, and any attempt to exterminate or utterly neglect the unfit, however defined, would undermine the principle of cooperation that society demands. No man who felt that he would be allowed to starve to death in his old age, for example, would feel much loyalty or sense of commitment to the society which left him to such a fate.

Darwin's important analogy between natural and artificial selection for reproduction spurred interest in the possibility of selective breeding of humans. A pioneer in this respect was Francis Galton (1822–1911), a first cousin of Darwin's, who studied human heredity by careful observation of the characteristics of identical twins and by tracing out attributes like high intelligence in certain families. He was among the first to apply mathematics to such problems, and gave convincing evidence that certain desirable human traits were hereditary. He coined the word "eugenics," from the Greek word meaning wellborn, to describe a new science: discovering methods of selective breeding by which to improve the stock of mankind.

The spectacular modern growth in our knowledge of genetics has shown that the problem of selective breeding of human beings is infinitely more complicated than Galton thought. Intelligence and other valuable traits are certainly not inherited in any simple and direct way, and there are many instances of men of great genius being born to the most improbable parents. In our own time few geneticists feel that efficient selective breeding of human beings is possible or, if possible, desirable. Even if we had all the necessary knowledge for undertaking this task and could foresee all the important consequences of matings, the task would demand such a regimentation of society, if undertaken on a large scale, that we might well enter the nightmare realm of Aldous Huxley's *Brave New World.*

Darwin's reception in his own country was mixed, as we have seen, and even among the most distinguished scientists. The great Lyell initially resisted Darwin's theory, and it was not until the tenth edition of his *Principles of Geology* (1867) that he accepted evolution as essentially true. The renowned Thomas Huxley (1825–1895) became an immediate "convert," however, and was the most eloquent expounder of evolution among Darwin's contemporaries. French biology was so much under the influence of Cuvier that Darwin's ideas penetrated only slowly into the fabric of French thought. The intellectual atmosphere in Germany was better for understanding Darwin, partly because of the influence of great German philosophers like Schelling, Hegel and Herder who had applied ideas of process and evolution to history and created, to some degree, a more hospitable climate for Darwinian concepts.

The leading German exponent of evolution was Ernst Haeckel (1834–1919). Like Darwin, he had gone on a long voyage of scientific exploration, in his case on the *Challenger*, while still a young man. One result of Haeckel's voyage was a monumental study of the Radiolaria, marine protozoa with beautiful, delicate skeletal structures. He identified four thousand new species of Radiolaria, and his study still remains a standard reference work on this group of organisms. It is interesting to conjecture that Haeckel greeted Darwin's work with such readiness partly because he too had spent many months in exploration and had come to see for himself the bewildering varieties of living things and the minute differences between them. A man who could distinguish four thousand species of a class of protozoa had the same eye for variation that Darwin had, and he must have been asking the same sort of questions that Darwin asked.

Haeckel was so struck by Darwin's theory of evolution that he applied it to embryology.* It was Haeckel who first propounded the idea that ontogeny recapitulates phylogeny, that the embryo in the course of development goes through the same stages the species passed through in the course of its evolution. Thus a human begins life resembling a protozoan in being single-celled; next it develops a double germ layer, then a triple germ layer, like various invertebrates. Later it develops and then loses the notochord, which is a permanent structure in those animals which come closest to being verte-

* Haeckel not only seized on evolution as a key to the whole of biological development, whence the application to embryology; he also realized that evolutionary theory would revolutionize the study of the relations of organisms to the physical and biological environment. It was Haeckel who gave currency to the term "ecology" for this branch of biology (1866).

brates, and still later, it grows fishlike gill slits. These too are lost as the embryo moves towards its maturity.

The notion that ontogeny recapitulates phylogeny became a very influential idea even against the opposition of Von Baer, the most eminent embryologist of the age, who was quite hostile to the theory of evolution. Haeckel's thesis is no longer believed to be true. Nevertheless, his idea had the merit of pointing out that embryonic development requires evolutionary explanation for its full elucidation. It is true that certain structures which have evolved into the permanent attributes of the adults of some species are "used" by life as intermediate stages in the embryonic development of other species.

As Darwin's ideas were diffused far and wide, the controversy over them became more rather than less intense. Everywhere scientists of considerable ability could be found ranged on one or the other side of the controversy over evolution. In America the struggle was carried on between Asa Gray (1810–1888), a distinguished botanist who favored Darwin, and Louis Agassiz (1807–1873), an equally distinguished naturalist who opposed him. It is of interest that Agassiz, a great admirer of Cuvier, tried to bolster the waning belief in catastrophism by his studies of glaciation. Agassiz, after admirable and careful studies of geological formations, advanced the hypothesis of periodic ice ages which, although slower than Cuvier's floods and upheavals, could account for the extinction of so many species and their fossilization.

Darwin, in his *Origin of Species,* had omitted any discussion of the origin of man. He knew, of course, of the discoveries which had been made, starting almost a generation earlier, of ancient tools and other artifacts in layers of rock far older than anything permitted by biblical accounts of man's origin. Just three years before the publication of the *Origin,* the Neanderthal skull had been discovered and had touched off the controversy between Virchow and Broca on its antiquity, Virchow arguing that the "deformities" of the skull were of pathological origin and Broca maintaining that the skull belonged to a different species of man. In short, during the period that Darwin was working on the *Origin of Species,* evidence was accumulating that man too was part of the evolutionary process. Even if Darwin did not consider the problem in his great book, the implications of his doctrine were clear and others raised the question of human evolution for him. In 1871, however, Darwin published another remarkable book, *The Descent of Man,* in which he gathered the evidence for human evolution. The archaeological evidence was still not abundant. After the Neanderthal skull, no further finds of human fossils were made until 1891, when parts of Java man, *Pithecanthropus erectus,* were discovered. Darwin's argument stressed, therefore, abundant data from comparative anatomy and especially the vestigial character of a number of human structures, which he interpreted as indicators of man's evolutionary history.

Since Darwin's book on human evolution more and more direct evidence has been uncovered of our now extinct forerunners, and the broad outlines of human evolution are now quite clear. The process of inserting man into the evolutionary scheme of life, which his book really initiated, has long been completed, whatever gaps there may be in our knowledge.

VI *Mendel and Genetics: The Stability of Life*

Darwin's was the first great scientific theory built largely on the notion of chance. Since his time "chance" has even entered the domain of physics, long the exemplary science for illustrating what is meant by "the eternal laws of nature," but well before quantum physics biology had constructed its greatest theoretical structure on a foundation which gave a preeminent role to chance and constant change. Variation of species, in Darwin's view, took place in all directions possible for species and in small degrees. Nature somehow realized the widest number of possible variations, and nature ruthlessly selected what would survive, if we may for a moment make cautious use of anthropomorphic terms.

The crucial weakness of Darwin's theory lay in the lack of any accurate understanding of the mechanisms of both variation and heredity. Nevertheless, a cardinal stipulation that Darwin made in his theory was that those variations which proved adaptive should be inheritable. Otherwise evolution could never have occurred. A corollary of this all-important part of his general theory was that variant individuals must not crossbreed, for Darwin was convinced, as were all biologists of his time, that crossbreeding of variant species would produce a blending of traits. How then could a variant type of species be preserved unless it mated with a variant quite like itself? How otherwise would variations be accumulated to lead eventually to a new species? How, given the small variations that Darwin postulated and the great likelihood of random interbreeding in any population, would a variation not be swallowed up, so to speak, by the effects of blending?

It was a long time before it was generally realized among biologists that crossbreeding does not produce blending of specific unit characters of inheritance. In fact, it was not realized for a long time that there actually were unit characters of inheritance, that inheritance was, in modern terminology, "particulate." For example, the crossbreeding of long-haired sheep with short-haired sheep to produce sheep whose hair was of intermediate length involved a whole cluster of hereditary units governing this characteristic and not one specific trait at all. Most if not all of the evidence Darwin had at his disposal seemed to show that there were no specific units of inheritance which could persist in a population without the reinforcing effect of constant and immediate inbreeding of particular variants. Latency of hereditary traits was even less understood. It had long been known that a trait would skip a generation or two and reappear, but there seemed to be little pattern or regularity to this phenomenon. It seemed to be accidental rather than determined by any law or principle.

We know now that inheritable traits will be conserved in a population, even when they have disappeared in the visible organism, and will reappear in some individuals of a later generation under specific conditions of interbreeding. We also know that certain characteristics of the phenotype, the visible organism, are derived from single hereditary factors and others are the result of multiple factors of an irreducible sort working together. Until the unit concept of hereditary traits with its corollary of the persistence and regular re-emergence of some traits from a latent condition became clearly understood, the theory of evolution remained vulnerable to serious criticism; how serious, we shall soon see.

Darwin was perfectly aware that the nature of heredity had to be thoroughly understood if his theory of evolution was to be rounded out to completion, and he pondered the question long and hard. The results appeared in a two-volume work, published in 1868 under the title *The Variation of Animals and Plants under Domestication.* It is an astonishing fact of the history of biology that Darwin's theory is nothing less than a revival of the ancient theory of pangenesis, modified to take account of the objections Aristotle raised against it. After considerably more than two thousand years, the greatest biologist of his time had no more to work with, eloquent testimony to the fact that much of our fundamental biological knowledge is of very recent date.

Heredity occurred, according to Darwin, through the process of pangenesis, which, as we have seen, means that the whole organism reproduces itself. This occurs as follows: all cells and even cell structures produce minutely small bodies called "gemmules" or "pangenes." The gemmules are all of a special type and correspond to the cells and cell structures that produce them. Dispersed from their points of origin, they gather in the sex cells, both the ova and the spermatozoa, so that each gamete will contain gemmules of every kind, from every type of cell and cell structure. With fertilization these gemmules become part of the next generation. As the fertilized egg begins to develop, gemmules combine with corresponding gemmules to re-create the cell structures and cell types from which they originated in the bodies of the parents. Once the fundamental structures of the organism are reconstituted by the agglomeration of gemmules, the processes of cell division and differentiation begin. Darwin had to admit that gemmules existed in enormous numbers and considerable variety, since they had to "represent" and re-create, in germ, all parts of the body. He had noted in his experiments in breeding plants and animals the well-known fact that traits would skip a generation or so, although he did not realize that there was an exact pattern to this phenomenon. To account for this he hypothesized that some gemmules might remain inactive in the first generation and become active in a subsequent one, although he could offer no reason why this should be so. In this idea we can see Darwin's attempt to answer one of the objections Aristotle raised to the version of pangenesis current in his own time: that it did not account for the fact that a child might resemble its grandparents instead of its parents.

Gemmules, like sex cells, were being produced all the time by organisms, and moreover, they would reflect the condition of the adult cells at the time of their production. This would permit characteristics that had been acquired at any time during the lifetime of a parent to be transmitted to the offspring. In this part of his theory, Darwin effectively contradicted the essentials of the line of argument he had adopted in the *Origin* and allowed for the inheritance of acquired characteristics: His contempt for Lamarck was not on the basis of whether or not acquired characteristics might be inherited but on the more fanciful Lamarckian notion of a "will" as instrumental in evolution.

According to this view, every change in the body would be reflected in the production of a new or altered kind of gemmule. These would be transmitted to the gametes and so perpetuate the change. On the other hand, more active gemmules from one parent might dominate the less active gemmules of the other parent so that, for example, the acquired characteristic would not be made manifest. Wherever a child resembled one parent more than the other, it could be assumed that the dominant parent had more numerous or more potent gemmules. Pangenesis could even explain sex-linked characteristics, such as color blindness, if one assumed that the gemmules for this trait would remain inactive in one sex, the woman in this case, and become active in the other.

This theory, as I have mentioned, contradicts the implicit and explicit views of variation and heredity which we find in the *Origin.* In that work, environment, whether physical or biological, acted on variations produced in a "spontaneous" or, if you like, unexplained manner. Environment did not, in itself, create the variations either in some direct manner or through the agency of entities like gemmules. To argue, as Darwin did later, that the environment produces directly inheritable modifications in the organism is to concede a good deal of ground to Lamarck.

Now Darwin, of course, had never seen a gemmule or a pangene. They were hypothetical entities with hypothetical properties, "fictions," if you like, required to explain the observable facts of heredity. Their hypothetical character is no objection to them. Atoms and molecules were hypothesized by physicists and chemists long before there was any considerable evidence for their existence and very long before much was known about their structure or properties. The same was true for the concept of the "gene," as we shall see. Indeed, our definitions of these fundamental units have changed with our increasing knowledge of the properties of matter, nonliving or living, as the case may be.*

In the light of what was known of heredity in Darwin's time, his theory was a plausible one. It helped to explain some important facts, such as the improvement of stock by selective breeding. If a breeder of cattle continually mated cattle for size, he would in Darwin's view be mating cattle which continually made gemmules for larger component parts. Repeated for generations, such a process would eventually eliminate gemmules for small size from the strain and produce a new

* Darwin was not alone in his time in speculations concerning the material basis of heredity. If he talked of "gemmules," Herbert Spencer talked of "physiological units," Haeckel of "plastidules," Weismann of "ids," and later on, De Vries of "pangens."

breed of cattle. In any case, however inadequate this theory may be in the light of modern knowledge of genetics, it held its ground with no competitors until the turn of the century.

While Darwin was pondering these problems and well before he published his work on variation and heredity, the foundations of modern genetics were being laid in a quiet monastery garden in Brün, Austria, by Gregor Mendel (1822–1884), an Augustinian monk. Mendel, in addition to his priestly duties, taught physical science to schoolchildren and cultivated a lively interest in botany. He had been well trained in Vienna in mathematics and physical science and came to his genetical studies with the kind of background which had inculcated in him the conception of science as measurement. It is an ironic fact that this distinguished scientist failed his qualification examinations to teach science in the secondary schools and did poorest, in the opinion of his examiners, in biology! He continued to teach the younger students, however, and was eminently successful with them.

Mendel became interested in plant hybridization and the monastery garden became his laboratory. There had been a long tradition of experiments in plant hybridization which had resulted in a sizable amount of data. Since it was largely the work of professional gardeners, florists and agriculturists, it was simply "empirical," that is, intellectually unorganized and essentially unexplained. You might find out how to cross one flower with another to get an unusual hybrid and the like, but not the slightest indication of how this happened at all. Indeed, during the late seventeenth and early eighteenth centuries there was widespread interest in breeding new varieties of flowers, and tulips were a favorite flower for such experiments. So great was this interest in tulips that large sums were paid for new and exotic varieties by collectors, and the wits of the day referred to "tulipomania" and "tulipomaniacs."

Some serious botanists had, of course, been interested in understanding the phenomena of hybridization, and well before Mendel the German botanist Josef Kölreuter (1733–1806) had noted the crucial fact that hybrids might resemble one or both parents as well as appear blended. Nevertheless no one, including Darwin himself, who had also experimented with plant hybridization, was able to so formulate the problems involved that they were susceptible to experimental study. The available facts remained obscurely related to one another and essentially unexplained.

In 1857 Mendel began a long series of studies on hybridization in peas, which lasted eight years and the results of which were described in two papers published one in 1866 and the other in 1869. The first paper is his famous masterpiece and was originally presented to the Natural History society of Brünn.

Mendel took up his researches in a very different way from any of his predecessors who had worked with hybridization. It now seems evident that he had a clearly formulated hypothesis concerning both the unit character of hereditary traits and the mathematical possibilities which would necessarily govern the combinations of such traits. He knew, in short, what sort of thing he was trying to find out, and this is perfectly evident in his excellent choice of the proper experimental organism. How important his choice of peas was we shall see, for when Mendel tried, at the suggestion of Nägeli, to replace his peas with hawkweed, he could not get the same results and even came to doubt the universality of his findings. Mendel did not know—no one did—that the ovule of the hawkweed was capable of reproducing without being fertilized, so that an unknown number of his attempted crossings of hawkweed were not crossings at all, although he thought they were. Why then, with both luck and intelligence, did Mendel pick peas for his researches?

For one thing, peas in a large number of varieties were easily available. Moreover, they grew rapidly and were quite easy to cultivate. These are perfectly sensible reasons for choosing a particular organism, as anyone can see. However, other properties of peas testify to more of Mendel's scientific acumen. If Mendel was going to crossbreed different varieties of peas, he had to be certain that all the offspring of any crosses would themselves be fertile or his experiments would have ended with the first generation. Peas, as everyone knew, would not produce sterile progeny if crossbred.

He also had to pick a plant so constructed that the chances of accidental pollination, especially accidental self-pollination, could be kept to a minimum. Now the anthers and the stamen of the pea flower are completely enclosed by petals. The usual mode of fertilization in these plants is self-fertilization, the pollen of the anther falling on the stigma of the same flower. Moreover, the anthers of the pea flower mature earlier than the stigma. It is therefore possible to remove the anthers before they mature and pollinate the stigma of one plant with the pollen of a plant of another variety. Since the reproductive organs are enclosed by petals, there is no chance of accidental cross-pollination through wind or insects, and the removal of the anthers eliminates the danger of self-fertilization. While accidental pollination is possible with pea flowers, it is relatively rare, and Mendel was safe in assuming that it did not occur.

More than once, as we have seen, the success or failure of a project in experimental research has hinged on the choice of the right organism, whether selected by luck or sharp intelligence or both. A recent example might illustrate this point even more forcefully than the example of Mendel. More than fifty years ago a number of chemists tried to extract active chloroplasts, the small green packages of chlorophyll in plant cells, from a variety of different plants in order to try to study cell metabolism in the test tube, so to speak. Sunflowers, geraniums and other plants were tried, but they would not yield active chloroplasts. Some thirty years after, other workers using the same techniques, extracted active chloroplasts from spinach. It is now known that even with the most refined laboratory procedures, active chloroplasts cannot be extracted from the plants that the earlier workers had tried. Had they started with spinach, the course of studies in cell metabolism would have been quite different. This, of course, is a case of pure luck, yet some degree of good fortune entered also into Mendel's choice, as his attempts to study hawkweed show. If peas had been capable of parthenogenetic reproduction, he would have gotten very confusing results, although he would, as a diligent investigator, probably have tried peas later on.

Mendel not only chose the right organism but he approached the problem of inheritance in a fresh way. His predecessors among both plant and animal breeders had interbred varieties that were different in many traits. The usual consequence of such mating is the production of offspring of blended or intermediate appearance. Occasionally, rather seldom, an offspring might look more like one parent, but this did not seem to be statistically significant or to follow a regular pattern. For want of anything better, Darwin had to accept the notion that the results of crossbreeding were generally blends, even though it created a tremendous difficulty for his own theory of natural selection. The difficulty was presented to Darwin by an English engineer, Fleeming Jenkin, who posed the problem this way: granted that crossbreeding results in a blend, what are the chances of a variant individual transmitting its variation to its offspring? It would seem impossible, for the new variant has to mate with an unchanged member of its species and its particular variation will be diluted in the offspring of that union. It would not take many generations for the variation to disappear by a kind of dissipation throughout the population. Even with his elaborate theory of pangenesis, Darwin could not entirely escape this problem since his version of heredity did not eliminate the notion of blending in inheritance.

Mendel had the brilliance and originality to concentrate his study on very specific characteristics, to look at only one small feature at a time and see how it was inherited for many generations. Although he detected some twenty-two characteristics of peas as possible features to study, he settled on seven, each of which existed in two varieties:

Characteristic	*Varieties*
Seed shape	round or wrinkled
Seed color	yellow or green
Seed coat color	colored or white
Pod shape	inflated or wrinkled
Pod color	green or yellow
Flower position	axial or terminal
Stem length	long or short

After establishing that all the varieties of peas he chose would breed true, he crossed all the paired varieties for each characteristic, round seed shape with wrinkled seed shape, yellow seed color with green seed color, and so on. The result contravened all the assumptions that previous experimenters had made. The plants of the first filial generation, now denoted by the symbol F_1, were not intermediate in respect to the varieties of a characteristic but were like one of the parents (P, for parent generation) *and only one.* If peas with yellow seeds were crossed with peas with green seeds, all of the offspring would have yellow seeds. Mendel concluded that one variety of a characteristic would be *dominant* and that the other which did not appear was *recessive.* For the characteristics chosen for study the following varieties would be either dominant or recessive:

Dominant	*Recessive*
round seed	wrinkled seed
yellow seed	green seed
colored seed coat	white seed coat
inflated pod	wrinkled pod
green pod	yellow pod
axial flowers	terminal flowers
long stem	short stem

These results were interesting and important, but Mendel had an astonishing ability to probe a problem deeply. He realized that the cross between colored and white seed coat (abbreviated colored × white) would produce plants identical to the colored parent. The progeny of such a cross would, in fact, look the same as that of plants produced by colored × colored, even though the parents of the two crosses were different. The parents, moreover, were all true-breeding strains, whether of the same or opposite variety. What had happened to the recessive trait? Was it lost forever or might it turn up in a still later generation? Mendel then allowed the peas of the F_1 generation to *fertilize themselves*, as they usually do, and discovered that the second filial generation, F_2, gave rise to plants in which both dominant and recessive characters were manifest. The recessive trait, white seed coat, was latent in the F_1 generation but appeared in the F_2 generation.

Mendel then did what other people might not have done. He counted the offspring of the F_2 generation and discovered that plants showing the dominant trait and plants showing the recessive trait appeared in the proportion of 3 dominants to 1 recessive. This ratio was the same for all of the varieties Mendel worked with, and he concluded that not only were there rules of inheritance but that these rules were the same for each of the varieties tested.

Mendel carried his experiments through to another generation. He allowed the plants of the F_2 generation which showed the recessive trait to fertilize themselves, and found that they all bred true, producing plants like themselves. In our example, the one plant out of four in the F_2 generation with white seed coat would produce nothing but plants with white seed coats. The three plants out of four which showed the dominant trait, i.e. colored seed coats, would, upon self-fertilization, give the following results: one of the three would breed true and give plants with colored seed coats, the other two would give plants with colored and white seed coats in the ratio of 3 to 1, just like the plants of the F_1 generation.

How did Mendel explain these remarkable and unexpected results? At this point, it is best to use our modern terminology and refer to the basis of a single inherited character as a "gene," where Mendel spoke of traits and factors, and use the terms, introduced much later, of "phenotype" for the visible appearance of the organism and "genotype" for its hereditary constitution. The modern term "allele" refers to the alternative forms of the same gene: i.e., a gene controlling height may exist in two alternative forms, one for tallness and the other for shortness.

Mendel had a keen insight into the mathematics of combinations and he hypothesized that the results of his experiments could be formulated on the basis of four propositions of an essentially mathematical nature. They would run as follows, if we take the gene controlling height in peas as our example:

1. Pea plants will carry two kinds (alleles) of height-determining factors (genes), one factor which produces tall plants and another which produces short ones. The factors may be dominant or recessive, but not both. In either case the factors exist as pairs of elements, either two for tallness, *TT*, which we indicate with a large *T* since this factor happens to be dominant, or two for shortness, *tt*, which we write with a small letter since it is recessive, or one for shortness together with one for tallness, *Tt*. These three abbreviations represent all of the possible *genotypes* in pea plants in respect to height.

In modern terminology coined by William Bateson (1861—1926) the combination *TT* is referred to as homozygous for the dominant—"homozygous" from the Greek roots meaning the yoking or joining of likes; *tt* is homozygous for the recessive; and *Tt* is heterozygous, from the Greek roots meaning the joining of unlikes.

2. Of the paired elements carried by a parent, only one element of each pair will enter a gamete and be passed on to the offspring. The offspring will therefore have a factor made of paired elements with one element deriving from one parent and the other from the second parent. A parent with genotype *TT* will produce gametes containing *T* only; one with the genotype *tt*, gametes containing *t* only; and a parent with the genotype *Tt*, two kinds of gametes in equal numbers, *T* and *t*. Remember that only one element of the pair which makes a Mendelian factor enters the gametes. After fertilization, the

newly constituted pair will have one element from one parent and one from the other. If a *T* gamete meets another *T* gamete, the next generation will have the genotype *TT* and so on.

3. The chances of one element from one parent meeting up in fertilization with any one element from the other parent are equal. If the gametes *T* and *t*, produced in equal numbers by a parent of the genotype *Tt*, fertilize gametes *T* and *t* produced by a second parent of the same genotype, the chances are equal for the following different combinations: *TT*, *Tt*, *tT*, *tt*. It is obvious that *Tt* and *tT* are the same and will constitute half the result.

4. In the case of dominant factors, the individual will manifest the dominant trait regardless of whether he carries two or only one of the elements for tallness. Thus *TT* or *Tt* will both be tall. In the case of the recessive factor, the individual will have to have both of the elements for shortness, *tt*, if the recessive trait is to appear in the phenotype.

In other words Mendel postulated that a long or tall plant, for example, is such because it has a factor, a gene, *TT*, and that a short plant is short because it has a gene, *tt*, the allele of the other. Now, Mendel continued, the gametes of *TT* will carry the *T* gene and the gametes of *tt* will carry the *t* gene. If we cross *T* with *t*, the zygote resulting from the fertilization will carry both *T* and *t*, although the plant that grows out of it will look like the *T* parent since *T* is dominant. The plant will be tall and, in phenotype, it will be identical to its pure-breeding tall parent. However, its genotype will be different, for unlike its *TT* parent, it carries both *T* and *t*. Its genotype will therefore be *Tt*. When this plant matures, it will produce gametes. Mendel postulated, and this is most important, that this plant would produce two kinds of gametes in equal numbers. Some would contain *T* and others *t* but *none* would contain both. If these two types of gametes, produced in equal numbers, were to unite at random, we could expect in that generation, F_2, a ratio of three tall to one short plant. One of the tall plants would have the genotype *TT* and breed true; two of the tall plants would have the genotype *Tt* and would, if self-fertilized, breed just like the plants of the F_1 generation we started with; and the one short plant would have the genotype *tt* and breed true.

What Mendel described is now called *segregation* and these postulates, in a generalized form, constitute Mendel's first law. If a pure-breeding organism possessing a dominant trait, *X*, is crossed with a recessive *x*, the F_1 generation, *Xx*, is like *X* in phenotype. Segregation of these traits will occur in the F_2 generation, where we will find a ratio of three plants of the dominant phenotype, of which one (*XX*) will breed true and two will be like F_1 (*Xx*), to one of the recessive (*xx*).

In tabular form, the Mendelian law of segregation could be illustrated as follows.

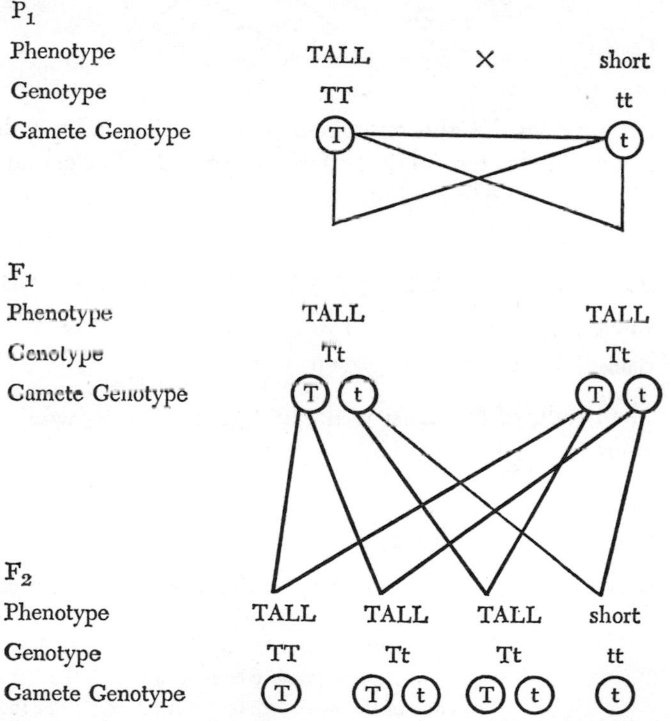

The same results can be tabulated in a more schematic form by the familiar Punnett square, so named after the geneticist who devised it.

P_1 TT × tt

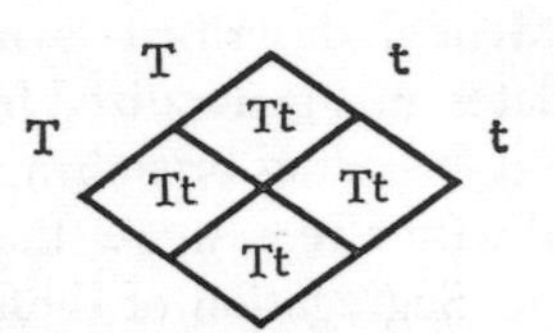

F_1

F_1 Tt × Tt

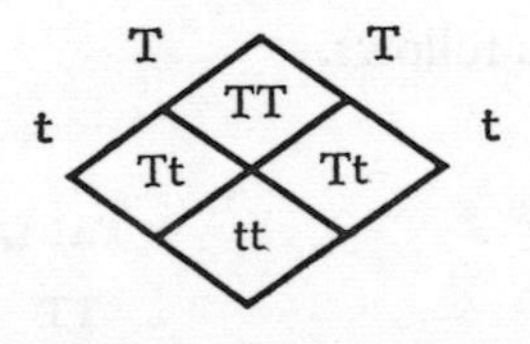

F_2

Let us consider the experiments illustrating independent assortment in greater detail. In tabular form the P_1 generation would look like the following:

P_1			
Phenotype	YELLOW & ROUND	×	green & wrinkled
Genotype	YYRR		ggww
Gamete Genotype	YR		gw

The results of this cross in the first generation F_1 would be the following:

F_1	
Phenotype	All plants YELLOW & ROUND
Genotype	All plants with YYRRggww. Remember that the hereditary factors in the parent genotype exist as paired elements which are separated in the gametes, no gamete containing more than one of any of the paired elements for a particular factor.
Gamete Genotype	(YR) (Yw) (gR) (gw) Four kinds of gametes are produced in equal numbers.

Now let us analyze the results of F_2 in detail. For the sake of simplicity I will indicate the genotypes of this generation with single instead of double letters.

Of the sixteen plants of this generation, nine will be yellow and round, three yellow and wrinkled, three green and round, and one green and wrinkled.

Nine plants { Phenotype YELLOW & ROUND
Genotype YRYR, YRYw, YRgR, YRgw, YwYR, YwgR, gRYR, gRYw, gwYR

Of these combinations, it is clear that there is only one YRYR, like one parent of the P_1 generation (segregation). YRgw, YwgR, gRYw, gwYR are obviously identical to one another and to the genotype of the F_1 generation. YRgR and gRYR are identical, as are YwYR and YRYw. There are in this group of a single phenotype four different genotypes in the ratio 1:4:2:2.

Three plants { Phenotype YELLOW & wrinkled
Genotype YwYw, Ywgw, gwYw. The last two are identical, so that this group has two genotypes in the ratio 1:2.

Three plants { Phenotype green & ROUND
Genotype gRgR, gRgw, gwgR. The last two are identical and this group too has two kinds of genotypes in the ratio 1:2.

One plant { Phenotype green & wrinkled
Genotype gwgw. This is identical to the second parent of the P_1 generation (segregation).

One of the most astounding aspects of Mendel's work is that with no knowledge of the cytological aspects of reproduction, on purely mathematical grounds, he predicted a pattern of reduction and reassortment of genetic factors which would eventually be detected in the actual behavior of chromosomes during gamete formation and fertilization. The proposition that the factors controlling a characteristic—whatever they might be like in their physical basis—existed in pairs, and that only one of each pair from each parent was conveyed to the next generation, was a pure piece of mathematical reasoning, since there was no physical model whatever for Mendel to work on. A mathematically clever reader will see that in the four postulates to explain segregation we have a simple sequence of axioms which will explain the ratios of F_2. Starting with P_1 and F_2, the only way to get from one to the other is to introduce the necessary intervening links.

The reader may recall that Weismann had predicted a reduction by half in his hereditary units called "ids" in order to preserve a constant number of hereditary units in the species; otherwise the number of ids would double in each generation in the very act of fertilization. Both Mendel and Weismann drew a logical consequence from their version of the unit concept of heredity. If the number of hereditary units is constant for a species, and both parents contribute equally of such units to new generations, these units must exist as pairs or be capable of being divided in two if the next generation is to receive the hereditary units in the same number and character as possessed by a parent.

Mendel was distinguished from all previous students of hybridization in that he approached his studies with a completely developed theory, mathematically based, by which the results of his experiments might be predicted before they occurred. His mathematical orientation was the fruit of his study at the University of Vienna under distinguished physical scientists such as Christian Doppler and Andreas von Ettinghausen, who laid great stress on the mathematical approach to scientific problems. Mendel viewed the units of heredity as discrete or particulate, and was thus in a position to understand the mechanism of heredity in terms of combinatorial mathematics.

His first proposition was that these units of heredity exist in pairs. When a plant forms gametes, whether pollen or ova, these pairs separate and no gamete contains more than one element of a pair. In short, the pairs *segregate*. At fertilization, which is a random process, pairs of genes are *recombined.* Thus, as we have seen, parent AA and parent aa make only A or a gametes respectively. When crossed the hybrid has the genotype Aa but it makes two types of gametes, A or a. When Aa is crossed with Aa, the result will be the expansion of a binomial $(A + a) \times (A + a) = AA + 2Aa + aa$. The ratio or proposition of genotypes is 1:2:1. Since A is dominant over a, the phenotype ratio will be 3:1.

The expansion of this binomial is a special case of what is more familiarly and generally expanded as $A^2 + 2Aa + a^2$. Only if the alternative gametes all exist in equal numbers will you get the 1:2:1 ratio. Since we are dealing with ratios or percentages and all the gametes exist in equal number and combine at random, each of the segregated pairs can be given the value 1. Thus the binomial expands as $1 \times 1 + 2 \times 1 \times 1 + 1 \times 1$.

In generalized form, this binomial evolved into the Hardy-Weinberg formula, which expresses the relative frequency of alternative genes in a population. Thus a gene p and its allele q will have a relative frequency expressed by the formula $(p + q)^2 = 100\%$ or 1. This will expand in the familiar way as $p^2 + 2pq + q^2 = 1$. What do these numbers mean? Let us consider a few simple mathematical principles. The chances of a given number of p's meeting an equal number of p's is the product of the two sets of numbers. Since in this case the numbers are equal, it will be the square. Thus if p is three, there are nine ways of a set of three p's meeting another set of three p's. This same reasoning applies to q. How do we get $2pq$? The chance of a number of p's meeting either the same or a different number of q's is, as we have seen, the product of the two numbers. But in this case they can combine in two different orders: p can meet q and q can meet p since we are dealing not with like meeting like but like meeting unlike.

In terms of alternative genes, p^2 can be interpreted as the number of homozygous dominants in a population, q^2 as the number of homozygous recessives, and $2pq$ as the number of heterozygotes. What is the practical significance of this interpretation? Consider the following problem and what the Hardy-

Weinberg law tells us of the practicality of simple-minded attempts to improve the human race by selective breeding. Let us conjecture a population of 100,000 in which five individuals are albinos. Albinism is the result of a recessive gene, so each of these individuals will have to be homozygous for the recessive to show albinism. Would prohibiting the reproduction of albinos remove albinism quickly? We would have to remove the gene from the whole population, so we would first have to ask how many of the people carrying the gene in a recessive state there might be. If q^2 is five, the number of albinos, our formula would read $(p + \sqrt{5})^2 = 100{,}000$. Taking the square of both sides and transposing we get $p = \sqrt{100{,}000} - \sqrt{5}$ or approximately $316 - 2.2$. $2pq$ will be pretty close to 1400 individuals carrying the trait for albinism! It would take about five thousand years of weeding out albinos to reduce the number of genes for albinism in the population by half!

The fate of Mendel's discovery is one of the most astonishing examples in the history of science of the world's not being ready for a great contribution to its store of knowledge. Mendel was unknown to the great scientific world and tried to interest Nägeli, the leading botanist of his day, in his work. Nägeli read Mendel's paper and carried on some correspondence with him, but he was supercilious about Mendel's contributions and felt sure that if Mendel carried on his experiments he would find, not that constant genetic factors would appear and reappear in predictable ways and ratios according to dominance or recession, but that there would be gradual variation of a random character.

Nägeli was a great proponent of Darwin and was himself interested in heredity. He tried to answer the objections of Jenkin to Darwinism by positing an inner drive which propelled organisms on a particular evolutionary path (orthogenesis), a theory which like all rather fuzzy notions explains nothing. He also worked out an equally obscure and untestable theory of heredity as late as 1884 in which he posited a substance called idioplasm as the stuff of heredity. It was an unobservable chemical network radiating through cells and between cells.

While this network changed during the lifetime of the individual, each embryo started out with idioplasm in its original condition. Apparently, in some rather obscure way, idioplasm controlled the continuity of the species through a chemical activity which reconstituted the same type of individual from generation to generation.

In spite of the fact that he was a botanist of high distinction, Nägeli had a penchant for rather mystical ideas. Perhaps that was one reason why he was unsympathetic to Mendel's researches with their austere symmetry and rigor. However, there are more important reasons for his lack of understanding. He, along with the other biologists of the time, was simply not ready for Mendel. It is true that Mendel's paper was buried in a rather obscure journal, but that by itself really offers no explanation of the general neglect. The paper was available and had entered the reference literature. Indeed, it was readily located when Mendel's work was independently rediscovered at the turn of the century by three different investigators. Interestingly enough, it would seem that the then current version of evolutionary theory may have blinded Nägeli's eyes to the significance of Mendel's work.

Darwin had postulated that new species came into being through a long series of small variations. Evolutionists therefore believed that studies in heredity, if carried on long enough, would demonstrate a series of small variations pointing toward the emergence of a new species. Their experiments in breeding, however, were carried on between varieties of species that differed in too many characters, so that their results seemed to show the blending of variations. Moreover, the simple Mendelian ratios were utterly obscured by their failure to select a single trait for study.

Darwin was convinced that any major or really discontinuous change in a species was most likely to be unadaptive if not downright detrimental. And to some degree Darwin was right. Most "mutations," as we now call such changes, are detrimental if not actually lethal, even when they are not sharply discontinuous. Nevertheless, mutations do occur and are of great significance for evolution, but, as we shall see, the manner in which they enter the hereditary material for natural selection to work on is more complex than anyone imagined for a long time even after the knowledge of mutation became part of the structure of biological theory. Moreover, there are other mechanisms by which the genetic material is not so much changed as reordered to produce variation.

In any case, the notion that variation was in some degree discontinuous, that it was "particulate," structured, so to speak, and not a blending spectrum of *continuous* gradations of minuscule changes, was rejected by the evolutionists of the time. Mendel's studies, if they had been applied to elucidating the evolutionary problem of the conservation of variations in a population, would have pointed to some degree of discontinuity in variation. In a sense, Mendel's studies seemed to point in a direction away from variation at all. He had nothing whatever to say about how new hereditary traits might arise, only how they are segregated and recombined in specific ratios and according to simple mathematical principles. There was apparently an enormous stability in the mechanism of heredity, too much for the purposes of evolutionary theory. Indeed, the Mendelian laws were much later generalized into the so-called Hardy-Weinberg law, which expresses in mathematical form the proposition that the hereditary characteristics of a randomly interbreeding population will remain in a constant equilibrium. The law takes account of the appearance of new hereditary traits by maintaining that such traits will also be preserved by entering a constant balanced equilibrium with all the other traits present in the population's "gene pool," the total of hereditary elements it carries.

Before Mendelian principles could be applied to evolutionary theory and solve the problem of heredity in such a way as to preserve the essential structure of Darwin's theory, a satisfactory explanation had to be given of how new hereditary characteristics—new genes, we might say—could arise, and of how genes work together in gene complexes of altering combinations to vary the phenotype of organisms. This was the work of a later generation.

Toward the end of the nineteenth century, there was a marked growth of interest among botanists in the problems of plant hybridization. Part of the interest was "pure" but a good deal of it was stimulated by the desire of various European governments to foster the growth of scientific agriculture to the end of increasing food production. It thus came about that three different botanists, working independently in three different countries, rediscovered the phenomena that Mendel had so brilliantly studied. They were Hugo de Vries (1848–1935), a Dutchman, the German Karl Correns (1864–1933) and an Austrian, Erich Tschermak von Seysenegg (1871–). Each of them made a search through the literature to find out if any previous work had been done on the subject, and all three found Mendel's paper. Ironically enough, the history of genetics would scarcely have been different even if Mendel had never existed! Another interesting point about this event from the historical point of view is that the rediscovery of Mendel's laws took place independently in three different places at about the same time—1900. The phenomena which Mendel saw and studied had, with a gradually increasing precision, been observed in the years after him. It seems now that the discovery of his laws was inevitable, and in a sense it was. However, that does not detract one iota from the genius of this solitary investigator, a genius that De Vries and the others acknowledged when they gave him full credit for the work he had accomplished.

De Vries made a contribution to genetics of the first importance in his pioneering work on mutations. Discontinuous variation had been thought of earlier, as we have seen. Von Kölliker, among others, had speculated that evolution proceeded by saltations or jumps, but little work was done on this problem until De Vries. He noted, in a population of American evening primroses that he was working with, the sudden appearance of a new type of plant of a pronouncedly different appearance, which not only bred true for generations but also obeyed the Mendelian laws in respect to its new properties. De Vries believed that he had witnessed evolution by jumps. Subsequent research has shown that only two of the hundreds of "mutations" De Vries described were true mutations, that is, the result of the formation of a new Mendelian allele. Many of his mutants were the result of rare combinations while others were the result of polyploidy, a change which sometimes occurs during the earliest stages of division of the fertilized ovum whereby the cell, and all subsequent cells deriving from it, have more than the normal complement of sets of chromosomes.

Nevertheless, in spite of these errors, De Vries' work was on the right track, and he gave an immense stimulus to research in genetics. If you like, his errors were fruitful, as others have been in the history of science. Perhaps a fruitful error is one with enough truth in it so that it asks to be corrected and not ignored!

One important scientific argument, advanced in Darwin's own lifetime, prompted some of the early students of evolution to entertain the possibility of evolutionary jumps even though the opinion of Darwin himself was against the view. The distinguished English physicist Sir William Thomson, later Lord Kelvin, had pondered the question of the sources of the sun's energy and the rate at which it was radiated. He also speculated on the rate of cooling of the earth from the incandescent state that it must once have been in. His calculation, based on the best physical knowledge of his time, was that the age of the earth could not possibly be more than forty million years. More probably it was less, perhaps as little as twenty-four million years. In 1869, shortly after Lord Kelvin made public these results, Darwin worried over the problem. He thought much more time was needed for evolution to take place. Indeed, he estimated that three hundred million years had elapsed since the laying of the Tertiary layer of rock alone! Darwin decided to trust the strong evidence from geology that much more time had passed in the earth's history than Kelvin had postulated. Nevertheless, the force of Kelvin's calculations was strong enough to encourage some biologists to speed up the evolutionary process by postulating jumps rather than gradual changes in variation.

Darwin called Kelvin's argument an "odious specter," and while it did not lead him to scrap his general conclusions, it left the time scale for evolution a problem. Biological and geological evidence of weight pointed in one direction and what seemed like equally weighty physical evidence pointed in the other.

The discovery of radioactive sources of energy eventually demolished Kelvin's calculations. The energy of the sun comes from a thermonuclear reaction and it has been going on far longer than Kelvin imagined any energy-releasing reaction could go on. The age of the earth is closer to four thousand five hundred million years than to the paltry twenty-five to forty million years that Kelvin allowed. Darwin, in fact, had ample time for his mechanism of evolution to work in. Fortunately, he was so convinced by the weight of biological and geological evidence that he dared to surmise that Lord Kelvin's conclusions would prove to be mistaken, even though he could not disprove them.

The effect of Kelvin's argument on some evolutionists is an interesting example of the way a theory may be modified in a direction later to prove useful in order to take account of a powerful objection later proved to be false. The necessity of having at least to entertain the idea that evolution may have had a markedly discontinuous character led to a rapid appreciation of the significance of mutations, however mistaken De Vries may have been about the vast majority of his instances of mutation and however unspasmodic evolutionary change has in fact been shown to be. With the work initiated by De Vries, the foundation was laid for that integration of genetics and evolution on which modern biological thought rests.

It is remarkable, when we reflect on the history of animal or plant breeding, how difficult it has been to grasp the true significance of the obvious. Animal breeders had long observed the sudden appearance of freaks or "sports," for example. Indeed, the now familiar dachshund was bred from such a "chance" variant, as were short-legged sheep. The latter were found to be a commercially useful breed because their legs were too short to permit them to jump fences! In addition, a large amount of data on hybrids among plants and animals had been collected during the eighteenth and nineteenth centuries. Yet no one until Mendel made any real progress in trying to understand what regularities might govern these phenomena, and his work was ignored for more than a generation! It is true, as I said before, that a genius can look at what everyone sees and think what no one else thinks. But even a genius cannot thrive in utter solitude and must exist in an intellectual climate in which his new thoughts are really understood.

We now know that evolutionary change is not radically discontinuous, spasmodic and jerky, just as it is not minutely continuous in a graded series of variations leading to a new species. As Darwin foresaw, large and sudden variations would be disadvantageous. Environmental conditions, at any given time, are almost always inimical to a mutation. It is precisely for this reason that most mutations are recessive; that is, they do not immediately appear in the phenotype, where adverse selection would act on them, but are conserved in a generally latent condition in the population. Natural selection acts on mutations, in those cases where the mutation confers some adaptive trait on the organism, *after* the mutant gene has become part of the whole gene complex and undergone recombination and segregation. Thus the appearance of a markedly new type of variant, like the dachshund and the short-legged sheep, is not the result of a simple change in a gene but the result of one or more small conserved mutations entering in complicated ways into the gene complex of the animal finally to produce what seems like a sudden change.

We now know also that the rate of evolution does not correspond to the degree of variation of a species or to the length of time of a particular generation. The rate of evolution depends on *how* the variations are acted upon by the forces of natural selection. A plant may exist in a thousand varieties, but if those varieties are not of a particular advantage or disadvantage in the specific environmental conditions in which the plant must live, they are not particularly significant from the evolutionary point of view. If the environmental conditions were to change, then perhaps some varieties might have more or less favorable attributes in *terms of these new conditions.* An organism such as a bacterium may pass through hundreds of generations in a few days. Even if in that time it produced many varieties, the forces of natural selection would operate only on those which conferred some advantage or disadvantage on the organism.

Moreover, the evolutionary history of any species cannot be thought of as a straight line pointing to the present form, as an earlier generation of evolutionists surmised. It is rather, as one biologist has expressed it, a zigzag line. G. G. Simpson has fully demonstrated that the various ancestors of the present-day horse look as if they were destined to turn into something quite different from what they in fact turned into. An early ancestor was a many-toed browser. He was later replaced by a many-toed grazer and finally by a one-toed grazer. Changing environmental conditions were at work to shift the line of evolution in one direction, then in another, then back in some respects to the first.

To some of his interpreters, Mendel's results seemed to show that the genetic mechanism guaranteed an almost granite-like stability to living things. An organism seemed like a puzzle whose specific hereditary traits could be combined in various ways to get different "pictures," but which would never otherwise change. Actually, the genetic mechanism is marvelously balanced to produce the proper degree of both variety and stability, or variety *within* stability. Genes mutate, segregate, recombine and can, during gamete formation, cross from one chromosome to another. All these properties make for variation. On the other hand, mutation is quite infrequent in the course of nature and most dominant mutations, since mutations are usually disadvantageous, eliminate the mutant organism quite promptly from the population.

Moreover, although a gene may change, it will never blend or amalgamate with another gene. On occasion the effects of two genes may produce what looks like blending in the phenotype, but the genes themselves remain discrete. One example of this is the fact that a cross between a red and a white snapdragon will produce pink offspring in F_1. This seems like a blend, but the F_1 plant contains both a gene which controls the manufacture of a red pigment and one which controls the manufacture of a white pigment. Both pigments are produced in such a cross and the result appears to be a blend. The F_2 generation will show perfectly normal Mendelian segregation: one red, two pink and one white. Similar conditions explain the AB blood type in man. The gene for A and the gene for B type blood both exist and function in such a person to make the particular proteins responsible for each respective blood type. Finally, genes produce stability because groups of them are linked together on the chromosomes, so that even in crossing over from one chromosome to another they travel in groups and therefore limit the possibilities of reshuffling.

Genes, moreover, do not work as completely isolated units but as parts of a gene complex. Therefore, the extent to which a particular gene affects the phenotype will depend on the activity of other genes. The case of the snapdragon also illustrates this point. Since the gene complex is modified in every generation by the effects of segregation and recombination of genes, the progeny of various crosses will often show a variation in the phenotype even when the particular unit genes remain in themselves unchanged. When the genes are arranged in different combinations, their *effects* will be different in the organism.

Natural selection acts, we should remember, on the phenotype, and that is the effect of the whole gene complex. Some gene complexes will prove to be more advantageous, *as a whole,* than others. One result of this is that some genes, advantageous in themselves, will nevertheless become recessive or be suppressed altogether. The most favorable gene complex may contain some genes for traits which are, from the point of view of natural selection, either neutral or even disadvantageous. Nevertheless, it would be impossible to eliminate them and still preserve the favorable characteristics of the complex as a whole.

This fact is not always a disadvantage, from the point of view of evolution. A trait which is disadvantageous in some circumstances can turn out to be quite advantageous in others. For example, in our own part of the world a wingless mutant of a fly is at a great disadvantage. It is helpless before any predator. But on an island continually swept by strong winds, such flies would have an advantage. They would not be swept out to sea, unlike winged insects and even predatory birds!

Another example is famous in modern biology. During the nineteenth century in England a black, "melanic" mutation of the peppered moth began to be noticed. It multiplied, but was soon eliminated by bird predators because it was so conspicuous against the background of bark and lichen of the trees on which it would rest. The mutant kept reappearing, however, and was just as rapidly eliminated each time. But as industrial progress progressively polluted the atmosphere, the trees became very dark from deposits of soot. Now the peppered variety of moth became the conspicuous one and the roles were reversed. It has been discovered that more than seventy species of Lepidoptera have been "melanizing" in the industrial regions of England!

Between the time Mendel made his discoveries and the time they were rediscovered there lay a stretch of thirty-five years in which important work was going on in cytology and the cellular phenomena underlying reproduction. In extraordinary detail, cytology was to reveal the microscopic structures and processes which "supported" the phenomena Mendel had observed with the naked eye. In the early twentieth century, one current of research was moving to amalgamate with evolution. A second current would amalgamate a generation's work in cytology with genetics.

The history of Mendelian genetics is filled with some of the most interesting ironies in the history of biology. It even seemed improbable, at the very beginning, that a monk in a small Austrian city, working alone, whose only academic affiliation was with an elementary school, should have made a discovery of such magnitude. It is even more ironic that Mendel should have been largely ignored. He read his paper in 1865, published it in 1866, tried in vain to interest Nägeli in it, and then, after a time, gave up scientific work to deal with the administrative problems of the monastery, then embroiled with the Austrian government over taxation. It is not strictly true to say that his paper was ignored entirely. It was mentioned a few times in the literature and was known to the American botanist Liberty Hyde Bailey, who cited it in his book on plant breeding published in 1895. Generally, however, it is true to say that it exerted no influence.

The theory which was to fill the lacunae of evolutionary theory first appeared as a problem for evolutionists. Mendel seemed to show that evolution was discontinuous and that hereditary traits were extremely stable, while Darwin believed in gradual small changes. There is evidence that Mendel was sympathetic to Darwin's ideas and even that he felt his theory could make a contribution to the solution of the problem of inheritable variations, but he never attempted any work in this direction nor did he even try to communicate his views to Darwin or to anyone else of eminence besides Nägeli.

De Vries, along with others, rediscovered Mendel's laws and suggested mutation as the mechanism of evolutionary change. Yet as we have seen, only two of the eight thousand cases he cited were mutations. Most of the rest were reversions to parental types in unusual hybrids. Yet his work was enormously fruitful and spurred research of the greatest importance. Mutations are, in fact, the ultimate source of genetic change, but they do not work in the way De Vries thought. Indeed, for a while it looked as if mutation could explain very little. Any mutations which are random and not related in some way to the environment of the organism at the time they occur simply cannot explain adaptation. Moreover, most true mutations are disadvantageous and even lethal. Genetics was finally integrated into the theory of evolution when it was shown that the characteristics of an organism are under the control not only of genes specific to them but also of genes working with or against each other in the gene complex. The gene complex may enhance or reduce the *effect* of a particular gene, and natural selection, after all, works on the effects of genes, not directly on the genes themselves. If the gene complex so functions that a particular gene is advantageous to its possessor, the organism will live longer and leave more progeny. If a gene, working in the gene complex, makes for effects which are less efficient in an organism's adaptation, it will not live as long and will therefore produce fewer offspring.

In a curious way, although genes are discrete and particulate and cannot be blended, their effects can, so to speak, be blended. An atomistic conception of heredity was indispensable if genetics was to be placed on a sound basis, but the notion of the gene as part of a continuum, as part of an interacting gene complex, is also important to our understanding of gene action. It is through this kind of analysis of gene action that genetics came to illuminate the theory of evolution. The effect of a gene can be enhanced or reduced depending on its place in a system of relationships with other genes. The gradual changes required for natural selection to act so as to foster adaptation are provided by such interaction of genes.

It is also of interest that the concept of a gene, what it was and how it worked, was at times boldly modified, in advance of much evidence, simply to suggest new lines of investigation. As we will see Morgan's assumption that genes were not simply logical constructions or mathematical ratios but material entities with actual locations was well in advance of the available evidence. It was open to criticism and received it. Nevertheless, Morgan's success demonstrates the fact that a theory may be worth formulating even if it seems less probable than alternatives open at the time *if* it can suggest questions worth investigating and open up a new stage of research.

We can see in the development of man's theories about inheritance special instances of two ways of trying to analyze the observed facts. Does the hereditary mechanism act according to atomistic principles of combination and recombination or does it act according to a continuum principle, with all kinds of intermediate modifications and blending of characters? In a simple sense, blending conceptions of inheritance were quite wrong, and certainly fruitless. Inheritance is particulate. But as knowledge of gene interaction was gained, some of the truth in the older theories has been extracted. Genes act in a system of genes. They are particulate and discrete, but from another point of view they act in a network of relationships, a kind of complex continuum which is as much part of what we mean by a gene as its atomistic character.

Both atomistic and continuum conceptions are important in science and should not be considered mutually exclusive. Does a biologist study the constituents of an organism or its total structure, that is, the way the constituents are put together to be more than the simple sum of the parts? Is it more important to analyze the constituent parts or to study the way all the parts are organized? The answer is, of course, both. "Reductive" and "compositionist" explanation, interpretation by atomistic principles and interpretation according to the idea of a continuum, are complementary and not exclusive. You have to know all the parts that go into a motor to understand it, but you must also understand that a perfectly good motor can be built using other kinds of materials or modifying the design.

In the final analysis, with all the twists and turns of theory, Mendelism profoundly modified the theory of evolution and the course of biological investigation. The first generation of evolutionists were largely concerned with that aspect of the evolutionary process which led to divergence and variety on the one hand, and to stability and continuity of types on the other. In practice this meant that the evolutionists of Darwin's generation were concerned with giving an evolutionary interpretation to all of the data of anatomy, taxonomy and natural history. Their emphasis was on elucidating and explaining adaptation in evolutionary terms. After 1900 and well into the thirties, the main thrust of evolutionary theory was to elucidate the mechanism of particulate variation and inheritance as it was affected by natural selection. What is now called the synthetic theory of evolution is the result of this amalgamation of genetics with evolution.

An interesting biological phenomenon that was discovered in the nineteenth century was the alternation of generations. This refers to the alternation of sexual and asexual methods of reproduction in different generations of the same organism. The two generations are often quite different in appearance from each other. Alternation occurs in both plants and animals, although it is far more significant among plants. Among animals only some of the invertebrates manifest this phenomenon, hydroids such as obelia, jellyfish, tapeworms and the like. In plants the phenomenon, in various forms and degrees, runs through whole great classes, especially the cryptogams such as mosses, ferns and horsetails.

The magisterial work on this subject was by Wilhelm Hofmeister (1824–1877), a German botanist who was virtually self-taught and who performed the incredible feat of becoming a professor at a German university without ever having earned any academic degrees. Amateurs in science were less common in Germany than in England or Italy, but even in those countries it is hard to think of an amateur who, lacking academic credentials, became a professor.

Hofmeister's studies were a triumph of meticulous observation and analysis. Sexuality in plants had been a far more elusive and obscure phenomenon than sexuality in animals. In principle, most if not all of Hofmeister's research could have been carried out in antiquity. Yet ancient botany had not advanced even to that elementary level at which one could begin to ask the right questions or recognize what it was important to investigate. By Hofmeister's era enough had been achieved in botany to delineate the problems and suggest lines of inquiry, but the work of this self-made investigator marks a huge advance in itself, a contribution of virtually unprecedented originality and power. His very amateurism, surely, played some role in enhancing his powers of observation.

VII *The Cellular Basis of Reproduction and Heredity*

Schwann's great contribution to biology had been to convince the biological world of the cell as a fundamental structural unit of living organisms. His notions of the physiology of cells and their origin, however, had made it impossible to think of them as having any connection with the mechanism of heredity, even if someone had been prepared to investigate them from this point of view. His influence can perhaps be discerned in Nägeli's theory of idioplasm, of a chemical network which contained the mechanism of heredity and which linked cells though it was not a part of their structure. As we have seen, Schwann had argued that cell formation was analogous to crystallization. Starting with the presumably structureless fluid he called the "cytoblastema," Schwann hypothesized that the nucleus of the cell crystallized out of the fluid. Next a cell membrane or wall appeared and the cell was essentially complete. Subsequent growth or differentiation of the cell was under the control of the entire organism of which the cells were unit structures. Cell growth and specialization conformed to the general plan of organization of the organism. Somehow, the organism saw to it that the cells coming into being were of the right sort for its various tissues and organs.

It became clear to some of Schwann's successors that cells arose from other cells under all circumstances. Schwann's theory of crystallization was meant to apply to the initial origin of cells, not to their subsequent reproduction, which he clearly recognized as taking place through growth and division of the cells.

By 1855 it had become abundantly clear to more and more investigators that cells never arose from any sort of structureless fluid or jelly and that they had no origin except in other cells quite like themselves. This conviction was summarized in that year by the great pathologist Virchow in the phrase "each cell from another cell." It is not immediately obvious, but Virchow's formula reversed the emphasis that Schwann had given to cell theory. It was not the organism as a whole which somehow shaped the cells and constituted them into their various kinds and agglomerations, but the cell which somehow constituted the organism. Yet in some degree, both of these statements are true. The long process of embryonic development with all of its growth and differentiation certainly involves all kinds of complex interactions between the whole and its parts. Virchow chose to emphasize the role of cells as the actual building blocks of the organism in order to stress their irreducible structural and functional nature. The cell was in his view the smallest unit which could be called living. It might have component structures and be made of complex chemicals, but only the cell as a whole could discharge the essential activities necessary to life. In general, this proposition is still valid. Some organisms and phenomena cannot neatly be fitted into the theory, but the same is true of many abstract definitions, whether in the sciences or in other branches of learning.

The next thirty or forty years after Virchow were to see remarkable advances made in our knowledge of cell structure and function. The complex nuclear changes which accompany mitosis, or exact cell replication, and the still more complex nuclear changes which accompany meiosis, the specialized "reduction" division which halves the chromosome number of sex cells, were to be clearly described. The cellular basis of all forms of reproduction was to be clearly established in the greatest detail, and the foundation was to be laid for establishing the cellular basis of heredity. These great observations and discoveries were, however, contingent on certain crucial advances in instrumentation and technique: major improvements in the microscope and the development of staining techniques for rendering transparent structures visible.

At the beginning of the nineteenth century, as we have seen, microscopes were still quite poor, although both glass technology and the science of optics had progressed during the eighteenth century. The great Sir Isaac Newton had discouraged progress to some degree by his belief that it would be impossible to correct chromatic aberration, and it was some time before physicists were convinced that it could be done. By the end of the eighteenth century it was shown to be theoretically possible for a lens to be corrected for both spherical and chromatic aberration, and in the opening decades of the nineteenth century several physicists were at work improving the microscope.

Among the first major improvements was that of the Italian astronomer and mathematician Giovanni Battista Amici (1786–1863), who turned his attention to microscopy and made one of the first successful achromatic lenses. However, he had such difficulty correcting spherical aberration together with chromatic aberration that he turned his attention to the design of a reflecting microscope. This instrument, like a reflecting telescope, magnified by means of highly polished mirrors, and the problems of correction did not arise. Limited in magnification and in other technical and mechanical ways, it was nevertheless the instrument by which Amici first observed fertilization in plants. The first successful lenses with good correction of both spherical and chromatic aberration were produced in 1830 by J. J. Lister (1786–1869), the father of the famous surgeon, Joseph Lister, and an enthusiastic amateur microscopist. These improved lenses were responsible for the progress in microscopy made during the next forty years or so.

The greatest single contributor to subsequent development

of the microscope was Dr. Ernst Abbe (1840–1908), a German physicist who joined the optical firm of Carl Zeiss during the 1870s. By 1878, under the technical direction of Abbe, the firm of Zeiss was turning out the best microscopes available. In 1879 Abbe designed the first practical oil-immersion objective, which gave much greater resolution and permitted much higher useful magnification than dry lenses. It had been known for some time that an objective designed to function with a layer of water or oil between it and the specimen would capture more light at a greater angle, thereby increasing its powers of resolution. In theory and practice, however, it was Abbe who created the first really successful immersion objectives. Beyond a certain magnification—about a thousand diameters—further magnification will be "empty." Objects can be made to appear bigger, but nothing will be made clearer. This is not a technical limitation but is imposed by the wavelength of light itself. However, even to carry the microscope to this limit of resolution, the capacity to distinguish or resolve small structures, required the introduction of oil-immersion lenses. Without them, the fine structure of cells would have remained beyond the capacities of even a well-corrected dry lens.

Somewhat later, Abbe introduced the familiar Abbe condenser to concentrate light on the specimen and effectively illuminate the superior high-power objectives he had designed. In 1888, he produced his crowning achievement in the so-called apochromatic objectives. These virtually eliminated the remaining chromatic aberration of the achromatic objective and were the result of years of research. After working out the theory of how such a nearly perfectly corrected objective might be made, Abbe found that the kinds of glass he required did not exist. He, together with others, developed new and superior types of optical glass at the Zeiss works in Jena which would make the construction of the apochromatic objective possible.

By and large, Abbe brought the light microscope to the degree of excellence it now has. There have been some improvements, of course, and new methods of illumination—phase contrast and interference microscopy, for example, have been of great value. Nevertheless, in theory and practice, the light microscope is pretty much where Abbe left it.

The finer structures of tissues, cells and microorganisms were still difficult to see, even with the improved lenses, because so many of these structures are transparent or virtually so. Even with improved microscopes there was considerable debate over questions which would have been simple to answer if the structures in question could have been made clearly visible. For example, did the nucleus of a cell divide during cell division? Or did it disappear, as it seemed to with the observational techniques available, and did each daughter cell make a new nucleus? The near invisibility of the cell nucleus and the fact that it often did seem to disappear made the latter version of events more plausible. Others thought they saw the nucleus pinch into two and one half go to each daughter cell.

Botanists for the most part thought the nucleus disappeared and was remade in each daughter cell, whilst most zoologists argued that it divided in two. What seemed like a debate over a fundamental cellular process turned out to be the result of differences of observation due to both the nature of the specimen and the inadequacy of instruments and techniques. Animal cells, such as the amoeba, for example, had a nucleus which was visible under the conditions of observation available, and when the amoeba divided, the nucleus did observably pinch in two. The nucleus of some plant cells could be seen, but the nuclear reorganization which accompanied division, that is, the formation of chromosomes, rendered the nucleus temporarily invisible. Since the amoeba divided without such nuclear reorganization, in what we now call amitotic division, the nucleus remained visible throughout the process. Even animal cells which divided mitotically would appear to lose the nucleus during division, so that the picture was quite confused, to say the least.

One interesting fact about the history of cell theory should now be clear: ideas about the complexity or simplicity of cells, about the simplicity or complexity of "protoplasm," "sarcode," "cytoblastema," or whatever term was used for the stuff of living organisms, rested directly on what instruments and techniques of observation were able to reveal. If Dujardin was able to conceive of the amoeba as a simple bag of jelly called "sarcode," that was simply because of what he saw through his microscope.

In addition to improved microscopes, therefore, it was necessary to find ways of increasing the contrast of cell and tissue structures, and a number of microscopists around the middle of the nineteenth century turned to the use of stains. In the early fifties carmine was introduced; in the sixties, haematoxylin and the first of the aniline dyes. At first these stains were used to give a uniform coloration to transparent specimens, but in the seventies, differential methods of staining were introduced together with improved methods of "fixing" biological material so that it would be preserved during the subsequent staining process.

Differential methods of staining were based on the fact that certain dyes had an affinity for certain parts of the cell or certain tissues. Thus, it was found that haematoxylin would stain the nucleus while eosin, among the first of the aniline dyes, would stain the cytoplasm. With this method the nucleus would appear blue and the cytoplasm red. By 1880, numerous workers had refined the techniques of fixation and staining to the point where the details of cells could be studied to a degree never before possible. With the introduction of the oil-immersion objective in 1879, techniques had reached the point where the greater useful magnification and the high resolving power of the new objective could be fully employed. There would have been little point in using this superior lens on structures which were nearly or entirely invisible in an unstained condition.

With improved instruments and techniques, it was inevitable that the nuclear changes taking place in dividing cells would be glimpsed by more than one observer. The first unequivocal if confused accounts of these changes came in the year 1873, and chief among them were those of Otto Bütschli (1848–1920) and Hermann Fol (1845–1892). There was still considerable confusion among these investigators concerning the old problem of whether or not the nucleus disappeared during division, and they gave various and conflicting interpretations of their uneven observations.

Walther Flemming (1843–1905), a German zoologist, brought order out of this confusion, and if any single person can be thought of as the founder of modern cytology, it is probably Flemming. If he did not, in a strict sense, "discover" mitosis, he gave the process its name, from the Greek word for "thread," after the threadlike chromosomes, and accurately described the major steps in this complex phenomenon.

Flemming was a remarkably gifted observer who really showed what the new instruments and techniques could accomplish. Like every gifted investigator he selected the right material to work on, and in his case this turned out to be the epidermal cells of salamander larvae. What were their advantages? For one thing, the cells of these tissues were large, and that made for easy observation. More important, this tissue was among the few in which mitotic phenomena are at least discernible in an unstained condition. This permitted Flemming to check his observations of the much clearer stained preparations against the living material. He realized the importance of this possibility because he was aware that the techniques of fixing and staining biological material might well produce artifacts. Moreover, the study of living material greatly assisted him in working out the order of the various nuclear changes in mitosis. Anyone glancing for the first time at a stained slide of tissues showing all the stages of mitosis will realize how difficult it is to say in what order they occurred.

Flemming noted that before division, in the "resting" stage of the cell, the stained nucleus showed intensely colored granular and strandlike material, which he called "chromatin" because it took up the stain so intensely. He noted that at this stage the nucleus was surrounded by a membrane and that there were one or more granular bodies larger than the rest, the nucleoli. The first sign that a cell was going to divide was signaled by the appearance of long, thin, threadlike structures, the chromosomes, intertwined in such a way as to suggest a skein of threads or, as he called it, a "spireme."

This first stage was later called "prophase," and Flemming was so gifted an observer and technician that he was able to see that the prophase chromosomes are double-stranded, made up of two thin strands later to be called "chromatids." Even now it is possible to detect this degree of detail only with the best lenses and the very finest preparations of suitable material! Flemming, by the way, did not use the word chromosome, from the Greek for "colored body," but referred to chromosomes as chromatin loops. The word chromosome was not introduced until 1888 by Wilhelm Waldeyer (1836–1921), and other terms which we now use to describe stages of the process, such as prophase, metaphase and anaphase, were not used by Flemming either but introduced in 1884 by Eduard Strasburger (1844–1912), a German botanist who was working out the mitotic process in plants at about the same time Flemming was doing his work on animal cells. We will, for the sake of clarity, describe Flemming's work in terms of the vocabulary which is now standard.

Flemming also noted that the prophase nucleus was marked by the gradual diminution and disappearance of the nucleoli. Metaphase, the next stage of this continuous process, was signaled by the dissolution of the nuclear membrane. At this time the chromosomes disentangled themselves from the spireme, assumed an individual appearance, and disposed themselves in a platelike arrangement perpendicular to the long axis of the cell and equidistant between two very small granules, the centrioles, visible only in stained preparations. The chromosomes were apparently joined to the centrioles by thin filaments making up a structure later to be called the "spindle." Asters, fibers radiating out from the centrioles, also appeared in this stage of mitosis, but like the centrioles they were visible only in stained preparations.

The next stage of this process, anaphase, was marked by the separation of the chromosomes into two groups, each one going to the opposite pole of the spindle. Flemming thought that each chromosome halved, and conjectured that the double strands he had observed separated, one chromatid going to one pole and the other to the opposite pole, a conjecture proved correct a few years later by Eduard van Beneden, the Belgian cytologist (1846–1910). In the final stage, telophase, the chromosomes were observed to become less distinctly thread-like, the nuclear membrane reformed itself around each separated group, the spindle and asters disappeared, and the cell divided. Finally the chromosomes disappeared and the nuclei of each of the two cells took on the granular appearance typical of the resting stage.

It eventually became clear that it is during the resting phase of the cell that the chromosomes become double-stranded. Mitosis separates the two strands, the chromatids, and the chromosomes as they are last seen in telophase are therefore single-stranded. When they first appear after interphase, they appear as double-stranded. With the later progress of cytology the so-called resting phase of the cell turned out to be something of a misnomer. While apparently resting, the cell is duplicating the hereditary material in an exact copy in preparation for its next division.

Meanwhile Strasburger was showing that plant cells behaved in a virtually identical way in mitosis, a process Strasburger called "karyokinesis," from the Greek for "nuclear motion." His results along with the work of others convinced Flemming that mitosis was a universal phenomenon in living things. True, plant cells lacked the centrioles and asters observed in animal cells, but otherwise the nuclear phenomena were identical. Flemming published a great monograph on the subject in 1882, illustrated with superb drawings and meticulous descriptions of his painstaking observations.

The next great contribution to the understanding of nuclear phenomena of cell division was the work of Van Beneden. Flemming and Strasburger sparked a debate over whether the number of chromosomes was constant. Flemming had correctly counted twenty-four in salamander cells and observed that the number was constant. Other investigators working with other organisms seemed to find a varying number of chromosomes in cells of the same species. Van Beneden presented an impressive amount of evidence to show that the number was constant in all of the various cells of an organism and that it differed only from species to species. (How remarkable an investigator he was may be guessed from the fact that for years the chromosome number of human cells was wrongly estimated at 48 and that it was only about twenty years ago that it was demonstrated to be 46. In view of the fact that certain defects such as Mongolism are due to an abnormal number of chromosomes, accuracy in these matters is important.)

In the course of determining the chromosome numbers of various organisms Van Beneden made a discovery of the first importance: the sex cells, both ova and spermatozoa, receive half the chromosome number found in all the other cells of the body. In modern terminology, the gametes have the n number of chromosomes while the other cells have the $2n$ number. Thus the human ovum or spermatozoon has twenty-three chromosomes while the fertilized egg and all somatic cells have forty-six. The intuition of Weismann and the brilliant mathematical reasoning of Mendel had found their structural basis, although the full implications of this fact were not to be worked out for some time.

Before we consider the work which placed both heredity and reproduction on a cellular basis, we might take a retrospective glance once more at the crucial steps in the long history of our understanding of the process of fertilization. Back in the seventeenth century, Nehemiah Grew had guessed that the flowers of plants were sexual organs, but did little to elucidate the process of fertilization. It was not until 1823 that Amici, using a reflecting microscope, saw a single pollen grain put forth a tube. Later in the same year he observed in a living specimen an ovary into which a pollen tube had penetrated. In spite of considerable opposition, Amici's belief that he had witnessed the sexual process in plants was confirmed by other investigators. In 1856, the German botanist Nathanael Pringsheim

(1823–1894) actually saw a motile sperm cell of the alga *Oedegonium* fertilize an egg cell.

In animals, the nature of the sexual process took somewhat longer to elucidate. The inconclusive debates between spermists and ovists which began in the seventeenth century persisted until well into the eighteenth and remained as sterile as they ever had been. The first important break in the problem came with the work of Lazzaro Spallanzani (1729–1799), the real founder of modern experimental biology. Spallanzani was a convinced ovist, but he was also a brilliant investigator who understood the role of experimentation in biological science as no one had before. All during the eighteenth century more and more organisms were shown to produce spermatozoa, and the old theories, as held by William Harvey, that the seminal fluid itself contained some power, an *aura seminalis,* which initiated embryogenesis were called into further question by the apparent universality of spermatozoa in semen. Obviously, the problem was not nearly as acute for the spermists as for the ovists. If the sperm contained a preformed embryo in the sperm head, that at least gave some reason for existence to spermatozoa. The ovists, however, had to account for them otherwise. For a long time, they thought them to be parasites, and indeed, Linneaus classified them with the protozoa. For an equally long time, there seemed to be no way to find out precisely what the role of spermatozoa was, if any.

In an attempt to determine the actual function of the sperm, Spallanzani devised some ingenious experiments. He gathered the semen from frogs, filtered it, and then tried to fertilize frogs' eggs with the filtrate. In a first series of experiments, he found that the eggs were fertilized, but realized that he might not have filtered the semen heavily enough—as was indeed the case—so he repeated the experiments after very heavy filtration of frog semen. He then found that heavily filtered semen would not fertilize eggs. He did not conclude from this, as we might imagine, that spermatozoa were the essential agents of fertilization, but that *both* seminal fluid *and* spermatozoa were necessary. His experiment was not designed to answer the question whether the spermatozoa alone were needed for fertilization but whether they were required in addition to the seminal fluid. As a convinced ovist, Spallanzani did not believe that the spermatozoa or the fluid itself made any material contribution to the embryo, and therefore did not design his experiment to determine that possibility.

In 1824 two French investigators, J. L. Prévost and J. B. Dumas, repeated Spallanzani's experiments, but asked further questions, so to speak, of the phenomena. They tried fertilizing frogs' eggs using spermatozoa which had been filtered out, and found that fertilization would occur with spermatozoa alone but not with the seminal fluid alone. This is a remarkable example of how what is essentially the same experiment can be used to give more information once the investigator knows what he is trying to find out.

Also in the eighteenth century, Buffon had reflected on fertilization and concluded that spermatozoa—"filaments," as they were called—were structural units of living things, a little like the pangenes of Darwin, out of which individuals could be constructed. Buffon thought he detected analogous bodies in ova and surmised that the embryo was formed by spermatozoa and similar structures in ova coming together to literally build up an embryo. Erasmus Darwin's odd notion that all warm-blooded animals evolved out of a primordial filament created directly by God was inspired by Buffon. Erasmus Darwin thought that this primordial filament, a spermatozoon ancestor of all warm-blooded animals, had been endowed by the Creator with the power of acquiring new parts and new propensities in the course of many ages, as well, of course, as being itself capable of reproduction. This is such a bizarre notion that those who find the work of Erasmus Darwin to be a true anticipation of the theory of his grandson might examine what he really thought a little more carefully. He was to some degree still using the old meaning of the word "evolution" as referring to the epigenetic view of embryonic development, since his starting point for the evolutionary origins of warm-blooded animals was the same kind of starting point assumed for embryogenesis: as the "ancestor" of an embryo is a spermatozoon, so the "ancestor" of all warm-blooded animals was a spermatozoon of divine origin!

In 1843 Martin Barry (1802–1855), an English biologist, dissected a very recently mated rabbit and found fertilized eggs with spermatozoa still within them in her Fallopian tubes, but his observations could not be confirmed and were generally disbelieved. In 1852 George Newport, another Englishman (1803–1854), continued the work of Prévost and Dumas and observed frog spermatozoa penetrating the gelatinous envelope of the egg and becoming embedded in the internal envelope which encloses the yolk. He was unable to trace them in the yoke itself and sought, but could not find, an opening in the yoke which would admit them. He did note, however, that the point at which the sperm entered the egg was the determining point for the plane-of-cleavage furrow. Newport, still under the influence of the speculations of Buffon, believed that fertilization required several spermatozoa. Darwin, in his work on heredity and variation, adopted this view of Newport's that several male elements would be necessary for fertilization, undoubtedly because the small size of the sperm relative to the size of the ovum would seem to indicate that a single sperm would not be able to carry a number of gemmules equivalent to that carried by the ovum. Unless the number of gemmules contributed by both parents were equal, heredity would be a rather matriarchical phenomenon. It was finally in 1879 that Hermann Fol saw that it was only a single sperm which fertilized the egg. His material, sea urchins' eggs, was much more suitable for this observation than frogs' eggs. If Newport had worked with sea urchins, the definitive demonstration of the process of fertilization might have occurred some twenty-five years earlier.

For a long time after the general introduction of cell theory into biology, it remained uncertain precisely what the sex cells or gametes were, from an anatomical point of view. Schwann, in 1839, had pronounced the ovum to be a cell and Von Kölliker in 1841 had shown that spermatozoa were at least of cellular origin. Yet considerable doubt remained. In 1861 the German zoologist Karl Gegenbaur published enough evidence to show that the ovum had to be regarded as a single cell, and was able to convince the biological world of this fact. By the middle sixties it was clear to all that both spermatozoa and ova were cells.

In 1873 Otto Bütschli noted that there were two nuclei in a nematode egg that had just been fertilized. As early as 1850, Nicholas Warneck, a Russian biologist, had observed the same thing in the freshly fertilized eggs of fresh-water gastropods. Neither Bütschli nor Warneck grasped the significance of their observations. By 1876, it had been reported that these two nuclei fused and Oskar Hertwig completed the account by noting, in sea urchins' eggs, that one of the two nuclei which later fused to make the fertilized egg came from the spermatozoon which had penetrated the egg. By this time, even before Fol's actual observation of a spermatozoon entering an egg, it had become clear that fertilization and reproduction were cellular processes, that two cells, one from each parent, fused in fertilization and that a new individual developed from a starting point of nuclear fusion.

The bare facts concerning the mechanics of fertilization and embryogenesis well established, attention turned to the study of intracellular detail. The reader will note that much of the work leading to clarification of this process was done with sea urchins. They were an excellent choice for a number of reasons. They were easily available, and it was possible to extract large quantities of both sperm and eggs from them in the laboratory. Unlike the eggs and embryos of frogs, those of sea urchins are beautifully clear. In addition, the earlier stages of development of the sea-urchin embryos follow a very accurate temporal sequence so that all eggs fertilized at the same time will develop in a strictly parallel way. This meant that the investigator could fertilize selected eggs at specific intervals and get a very clear picture of the sequence of events going on in the cell. It was thus quite possible to trace the course of the nucleus derived from the sperm—the so-called pronucleus—as it moved to unite itself with the nucleus of the egg cell, also called the pronucleus at this stage, to indicate that it would be "half" of the fusion or zygote nucleus.

When investigators turned their attention to the nuclear changes accompanying fertilization, however, sea urchins proved to be unsatisfactory. Their cells had a large number of chromosomes, and they were quite small and difficult to see. Another, quite different organism proved to be the better choice: this was the parasitic nematode worm *Ascaris*. Its cells possess only four large chromosomes, and they are easy to stain and study.

During the eighties, Van Beneden and Boveri worked out the nuclear changes accompanying fertilization in *Ascaris* eggs. They noted that in the process of fertilization the nucleus derived from the sperm, the sperm pronucleus, underwent changes quite similar to those occurring in the prophase of mitosis, that is, chromosomes formed out of the dense granular chromatin. Identical changes occurred in the nucleus of the ovum. Soon the chromosomes from the pronuclei of the sperm and the egg came together and arranged themselves on the spindle. The fertilized egg at this stage possessed spindle, centrioles and asters—what later came to be called the achromatic figure because it did not take up the stain which had an affinity for the chromosomes—quite like it does in mitosis. Indeed, at this point the fertilized egg was ready to undergo its first cleavage by mitotic division.

Now both Van Beneden and Boveri noted a striking fact. Two of the normal complement of four chromosomes in *Ascaris* cells came from the sperm and the other two came from the nucleus of the ovum. In modern terminology, the gametes had the haploid or n number of two, while the other cells, including the fertilized egg, had the diploid or $2n$ number of four. This process by which half the chromosomes come from the father and half from the mother was shown to be a universal feature of sexual reproduction. Gametes differed from all other cells in the organism in having half the number of chromosomes.

How were cells so constituted produced? Mitosis made an exact replica of a cell with the identical number, $2n$, of chromosomes. It had been long established that both spermatozoa and ova were cellular products and investigation showed that the spermatocytes, cells which produce spermatozoa, and the oöcytes, cells which produce ova, had the $2n$ number. There had therefore to be a form of cell division which reduced the number of chromosomes by half. It was shown that there was such a form of division, to be called meiosis from the Greek word for "reduction." Unlike mitosis, meiosis involved two divisions, a first which halved the number of chromosomes from the $2n$ number to the n number, and a second which, like mitosis, duplicated the products. The result of this double division would be that a single diploid ($2n$) spermatocyte would produce four haploid (n) sperm cells. The process of reduction division from oöcyte was identical, except that of the four final products, it was frequently found that one or more became polar bodies and were eliminated as gametes. With variations in detail, meiosis was a universal feature of the production of gametes. As mitosis accounted for the extraordinary stability of life, cells making precise copies of one another, meiosis was the mechanism for variety. Each new individual received half of his inheritance from each parent. Each act of fertilization changed in some degree the inherited material.

Thus, between the middle seventies and about 1890 a spectacular series of observations had worked out the details of mitosis, fertilization and meiosis, had placed reproduction and growth on a secure cellular basis, and had located the whole mechanism of heredity in the cell, although there was uncertainty concerning what structures of the cell might control inheritance. As early as 1866 the brilliant if somewhat erratic Haeckel had suggested that the nucleus contained the mechanism of inheritance, but the techniques and instruments of his time did not permit any verification of this hypothesis. In the eighties, hard upon the great work of Strasburger, Flemming, Van Beneden and Boveri, a good deal of speculation was going on to determine what part of the cell might control inheritance. Nägeli, as we have seen, proposed a very obscure theory in 1884, but in the same year and a little later four leaders in German biology suggested that the chromosomes might be the physical structures controlling inheritance. They were Hertwig, who had witnessed fertilization, Von Kölliker, who had placed embryology on a cellular basis, Strasburger, who had worked out mitosis in plants, and Weismann, the brilliant theoretician. We can see, then, why all of these four men were prepared, on the basis of their investigations or their prior thinking, to make the suggestion that chromosomes were the physical basis of heredity. How did their reasoning work?

Both parents seem to have an equal share in inheritance, the mother contributing an egg and the father a single sperm. Yet the difference in size between these two cells is enormous. After all, the eggs you eat for breakfast are single cells! The mass of even a small ovum is many times larger than that of a sperm cell. Moreover, careful examination of the ovum compared with the sperm shows that the ovum has the characteristic cytoplasm found in all cells, however big the yolk, while the sperm appears to have none at all. If whatever controlled heredity were in the cytoplasm, the influence of the mother would be many thousand times greater than the influence of the father (recall that Darwin favored the notion of multiple sperms in fertilization precisely because he needed equal numbers of gemmules to equalize the hereditary contribution of both parents to the offspring). What the studies on *Ascaris* had shown was that the ovum and sperm had two equal structures in the pronuclei. Both were of the same size and both yielded two chromosomes. Perhaps this equality would account for the fact that parents do play an equal role in inheritance.

A second point of a very suggestive sort lay in the fact that during cell division all of the most significant changes took place in the nuclear material. Most of the activity was on the part of the chromosomes. In mitosis, they appeared as double-stranded, and the whole division process seemed intended simply to separate the strands and to make sure that each daughter cell received the same number of chromosomes as the parent. The chromosomes thus seemed to be the only cell structures carefully and exactly transmitted in cell division, exactly "inherited," so to speak, by the daughter cells. They might well have a crucial role in inheritance. Meiosis, too, was suggestive. It was clear that meiosis kept the chromosome number of a species constant. If gametes were diploid, each successive generation would have double the number of chromosomes, and it wouldn't be many generations before no cell could contain them all. Meiosis was as exact in its way as mitosis. Moreover, the chromosomes of gametes seemed to be the only cell structures transmitted to successive generations in a precise number and manner.

Further evidence came from work on protozoa. Von Siebold had established protozoa as single cells in 1845, and experiments on regeneration in protozoa done since his time had shown that the part of the protozoan controlling regeneration and reproduction was probably the nucleus. If, for example, an amoeba were cut in two, both parts would survive the operation, but the only part capable of reconstituting itself as a complete organism and reproducing was the part with the nucleus.

With the work on chromosome behavior, the conviction grew that the chromosomes within the nucleus were the carriers of the hereditary material. There were some problems at first with this notion, even though it became the working hypothesis of the leading biologists during the eighties. The nucleus in the resting phase, for example, did not show chromosomes, and some investigators felt that structures carrying the material of heredity must be permanent. Flemming, indeed, was so certain that this must be the case that he assumed that chromosomes must be permanent structures in spite of the fact that no trace of the threadlike structures could be found in the nuclei of resting cells. Actually, Flemming was not altogether wrong. It seems clear now that chromosomes, when they become visible, are like tightly packed coils, and that their uncoiling in the resting nucleus gives it its relatively homogeneous appearance.

In spite of these difficulties, some brilliant suggestions concerning the chromosomal basis of heredity were advanced during this period. As early as 1883, Roux suggested that the universally similar appearance of chromosomes in so many different species suggested that the threadlike shape must be of functional significance and confer some selective advantage. He thought that the individual hereditary factors which he called "qualities" were arranged in a linear way along the length of the chromosome. The chromatids which separated at mitosis must be duplicates and this must ensure that each daughter cell received the same hereditary complex.

The year 1902 marked a particular culminating point in the history of biology and it is defined by the work of two biologists, one a German, Theodor Boveri (1862–1915), and the other a young American graduate student, W. S. Sutton (1876–1916). The brilliant achievements of nineteenth-century microscopy had located the physical basis of heredity in the cell and had elucidated the reproductive process, whether simple cell division or the cytological processes underlying sexual reproduction. It was clear by this time to most investigators that the chromosomes carried the units of heredity, whatever they might be like. The further questions was how these units of heredity might be distributed among the chromosomes. Were all chromosomes alike or were the hereditary factors distributed among them?

In a series of brilliant experiments Boveri showed that a complete set of chromosomes was necessary if the fertilized egg was to develop normally. Sea urchins again proved to be the proper experimental organism, in spite of the fact that their chromosomes were numerous, small and hard to count. What made the sea urchin so useful for these experiments was the fact that it was possible, by surrounding a sea urchin's egg with a lot of sperm, to get two spermatozoa to fertilize one egg. This is not a common occurrence in nature, nor is it at all possible with the great majority of organisms. Fortunately for Boveri, it is with sea urchins. When such an egg is fertilized by two sperms, the events of mitosis become thoroughly irregular and an equal distribution of chromosomes to the daughter cells becomes impossible. A cell may get too many or too few. Boveri showed that embryos with an abnormal number of chromosomes developed abnormally. It seemed clear that a regular complement of chromosomes was necessary for normal development, strong evidence that different hereditary units were in different chromosomes.

In the same year W. S. Sutton published a remarkable study of the chromosomes of the grasshopper testis cells which finally correlated chromosome movements and distributions with the laws of Mendel. The spermatogonia of the grasshopper, the sperm-making cells, have the normal diploid number of twenty-two chromosomes plus one "accessory" chromosome, making a total of twenty-three. A year earlier, C. E. McClung (1870–1946) had suggested that the accessory chromosome was involved with sex determination, that in short, two kinds of haploid sperms would be produced by the meiotic division of the spermatogonia, one kind with the accessory chromosome and the other without it. The sperm with the accessory chromosome would produce a female; the sperm without it would produce a male. The grasshopper was an excellent subject for the study of the cellular basis of sex determination because its chromosomes are easily discernible and the accessory chromosome, the sex-determining one, is quite distinguishable from the others, the so-called "autosomes."

Sutton, following a suggestion made by T. H. Montgomery (1873–1912) in 1901, was investigating the problem of whether the distinct differences in size of the chromosomes making up the normal complement of a cell are constant attributes of the chromosomes or merely a matter of chance. Sutton noted that the chromosomes of the spermatogonia of the grasshopper could be arranged in eleven quite distinct pairs (plus the accessory chromosome) and that there were strong grounds for assuming that of each pair of homologous chromosomes one had a maternal and the other a paternal origin.

Study of the phases of meiosis going on in the grasshopper testis as the spermatogonia divided to produce sperm cells disclosed some other interesting facts. In the prophase of the first division of meiosis, the newly emergent chromosomes of the sperm-making cell came together in pairs for a while in what is called "synapsis." Sutton noted that the pairs that came together were those that corresponded in size and shape. He then observed that in the first division of meiosis, the one which reduces the chromosome number to half, the corresponding pairs would wind up in different cells. Now assuming that one of the pairs is maternal in origin and the other paternal, how would they separate? Would all maternal chromosomes go to one cell and all paternal ones to the other? Sutton maintained that all the evidence showed that it was merely a matter of chance how the separated pairs distributed themselves. To be sure, one homologue would always go to one cell and the other would always wind up in the other cell, but whether, in any case, it was the maternal or paternal chromosome which would end up in one of the two cells of the first division was merely a matter of chance. There were thus a great many different possible assortments of maternal and paternal chromosomes. In fact, if you think about it and draw on a little elementary mathematics, there are 2 to the *n* number or, in this case, 2^{11} possibilities for the distribution of eleven pairs into two sets. A great many different combinations of maternal and paternal hereditary units indeed!

Sutton's conclusion from his observations was that different chromosomes clearly played a specifically different role in heredity, and that the pairing of homologous chromosomes and their separation at the first meiotic division was of genetic significance. In fact, the behavior of chromosomes constituted the physical basis of the Mendelian phenomena. In a further paper published the next year, in 1903, he explained how this would be the case if what we today call genes, the hereditary factors, were thought of as localized on specific chromosomes. Now each gamete contributes one chromosome, a homologue, to the zygote. Mendel, let us recall, had argued that each hereditary trait was determined by factors which existed in pairs, for example, two for tallness (*TT*), two for shortness (*tt*) or one for tallness and one for shortness (*Tt*). If a single homologous chromosome carried one of these genes, *T* or *t*, and the other carried the same gene or its allele, we could explain how a new genotype is made from a particular cross. Mendel had also argued that of these factors, only one of the pairs determining the factor entered a gamete, but not both. A plant carrying both a single element for tallness and a single element for shortness would produce two kinds of gametes, one kind containing *T* and the other *t*. The separation of homologous chromosomes at the first meiotic division would produce precisely this result in the case of a plant of the genotype *Tt*. In fact, Sutton pointed out that you could directly substitute "chromosome" everywhere Mendel talked of paired hereditary factors. As he expressed it:

> Thus the phenomena of germ-cell divisions and of heredity are seen to have the same essential features, viz. purity of units (chromosomes, characters) and the independent transmission of the same; while, as a corollary, it follows in each case that each of the two antagonistic units (chromosomes, characters) is contained by exactly half the gametes produced.

In other words, if meiosis separates out alternative "traits," fertilization will recombine them in genetic ratios. Thus if germ cells combine, each of which bears either of two alternative chromosomes *A* or *a*, the result will be the genotypic ratios of Mendel, *AA*, *Aa*, and *aa* in the ratio 1:2:1.

With Sutton's work genetics and cytology came to illuminate each other and to share a common body of theory and techniques.

viii *The Chemical Basis of Heredity: Problems of the Future*

During the nineteenth century, after the work of Berthelot, organic chemistry advanced at a truly rapid pace and it was not many years before a flood of new organic compounds were synthesized and entirely new industries were founded. Biochemistry had to wait until our own time to achieve its most remarkable progress, but even here important work was done in the nineteenth century. By 1900 photosynthesis had been carefully studied and some of the essentials of the process had been clarified. The nitrogen cycle had been worked out, the chemistry of colloids was under development, and a great step forward had been taken in understanding the structure of proteins when the German chemist Emil Fischer (1852–1919) was able to show that proteins were built of smaller structural units called amino acids. In our own century progress accelerated. The details of some of the important metabolic processes were worked out, and we now have a detailed account of some of the ways in which a living organism captures, stores and releases energy. How recent much of this progress in biochemistry has been may be realized when we reflect that it was only about

1930 that enzymes, the all-important catalysts of chemical reactions in living things, were understood to be proteins, and scarcely ten years ago that insulin, one of the simpler proteins but still enormously complicated, was synthesized.

Two great nineteenth-century contributions of biochemistry to biological science as a whole were the discovery and partial elucidation of the process of photosynthesis, by which chlorophyll-bearing plants—the great majority of them—produce carbohydrates from water and carbon dioxide with the aid of energy derived from sunlight, and the discovery of the nitrogen cycle. Both of these discoveries illuminated and specified the interrelatedness of living things, and the clarification of the nitrogen cycle to an even greater degree.

Inorganic nitrogen compounds are absorbed by green plants from the soil (or sea water in the case of marine plants) and built up into organic nitrogen compounds. The animals which eat these plants use the organic nitrogen compounds to make their own substance. Excretion or decay returns these organic nitrogen compounds to the soil or the sea where bacterial action converts them into inorganic nitrogen compounds. Even though a certain small quantity of nitrogen is lost to the atmosphere, some atmospheric nitrogen is fixed by certain species of bacteria which grow on the roots of some plants. They have the property of being able to extract free nitrogen from the air, turn it into chemical compounds, and thereby make it accessible to the plants.

Three investigators were most important in pioneer work on the process of photosynthesis: the French physician-turned-botanist Henri Dutrochet (1776–1847), the German botanist Julius von Sachs (1832–1897), and the German physiologist T. W. Engelmann (1843–1909). The importance of nitrogen in plant life had been well known to the earlier generation of chemists in the nineteenth century, but the elucidation of the nitrogen cycle was the work of two French chemists, Jean Baptiste Boussingault (1802–1887), and the virtual father of modern organic chemistry and a distinguished historian of chemistry, Marcelin Berthelot (1827–1907).

Furthermore, modern work in biochemistry has shown not only the interrelatedness of living things but the extraordinary similarity in their chemical mechanisms. Metabolic processes in plants and animals, once thought to be so different, have been shown to be much alike. Fermentation, photosynthesis and aerobic respiration are quite closely related. Aerobic respiration is, chemically speaking, a process hooked onto the tail end of fermentation. Starting with the sugar glucose, fermentation begins through phosphorylation, the combination of the sugar with phosphoric acid. A subsequent series of stages release energy which is packaged in the phosphate ATP—adenosine triphosphate—and also yields carbon dioxide and alcohol in the case of a yeast, or lactic acid in the case of an animal, in whose tissues glycolysis, "sugar-splitting," will be taking place. So much for fermentation, and the very similar process of glycolysis which occurs in animals. Now if the proper enzymes are present, the waste produce enters the so-called Krebs or citric acid cycle. It is transformed through a series of simple organic acids into more energy packaged as ATP and water. This biochemical knowledge suggests that living things first obtained their energy through the process of fermentation which yielded carbon dioxide. Only then could photosynthesis occur, since it requires free carbon dioxide. Aerobic respiration came last as photosynthesis, creating oxygen, transformed the atmosphere.

Obviously, with all the progress in biochemical knowledge, there is still a great deal more to be learned. The biochemical details of blood clotting, for example, are still obscure, and the biochemical basis of brain and nerve function has scarcely begun to be investigated. Such problems, however complicated their chemistry, will probably be solved without causing any sort of intellectual revolution. Even if they are not thoroughly understood, the biochemistry of these and similar life functions seems to involve quite "orthodox" chemical reactions.

Although the science of biology has been and will continue to be immeasurably strengthened by contributions from chemistry, we must distinguish between biochemical progress per se and the contribution it may make to the solution of biological problems. How will our knowledge of the chemistry of living things illuminate the age-old problems of developmental biology? Physical as well as chemical factors of a complex kind are at work in development, and the developing embryo seems to be a complex aggregate of a number of developmental systems, with intricate relations between them, governed by equally intricate control systems involving "feedback," that is, various processes that are turned on and off as they are needed.

We shall soon consider the recent and remarkable discoveries which led to clarification of the molecular basis of heredity, the new "molecular genetics," but some preliminary observations concerning what biological questions can be answered directly by chemistry and what cannot might be in order. The mountain of biochemical knowledge we now have has amply illustrated how astonishingly similar the biochemistry of living things is. The nucleic acids which are the chemical basis of heredity in all known organisms are remarkably similar from species to species from a strictly chemical point of view, however significant structural differences among them may be in determining the final outcome of their activity. The nucleic acids extracted from an elephant are chemically closer to the nucleic acids from a mouse than they are to those of some organisms which resemble the elephant a lot more. The small ciliated protozoan *Tetrahymena* turns out to have precisely the same nutritional requirements as man. Like man, it has enzymes to make only nine amino acids of the twenty it requires, and must take in the rest ready-made from its food.

What is clear from evidence of this sort is that life uses fundamentally few basic chemical strategies for reproducing itself and for meeting its energy requirements. Organisms with utterly different biological characteristics and utterly different evolutionary histories may have, at the molecular and chemical level, remarkable affinities. If the picture that evolution gives us of life is one of incredible variety, the picture of life that we get from molecular biology and biochemistry is of astonishing similarities. The biological distance from a virus to a man is an enormous one from almost every point of view, yet some of the most important recent knowledge of the working of the genetic mechanism came, as we shall see, from work with viruses.

The point at which biochemical knowledge most clearly illuminates the classical problem of biology, that of reproduction and development, lies in the new triumphs of molecular biology and, in particular, molecular genetics. This new field stands in the same relation to classical cytology that classical cytology did to classical genetics. Cytology provided the explanation of Mendelian genetics on the cellular level and showed what components of cells continued the physical basis of heredity. Molecular genetics has taken this explanation down to the chemical and molecular level where we encounter the most elementary units of living matter. Each one of these levels supports and explains the other.

The crucial importance of proteins to life had long been known, and as knowledge of protein structure advanced, scientists assumed that the puzzling problems of reproduction and development would likewise be clarified. In an extraordinary sequence of discoveries, another class of substances, the nucleic acids, revealed themselves as central to understanding the nature of heredity and reproduction.

The first step in this revolution came in the mid-1930s, when an American biochemist, Wendell Stanley (1904–), tried to extract the pure virus from tobacco plants infected with tobacco mosaic disease. Enzymes, which had been shown to be proteins, had only recently been extracted in a pure state. Stanley, assuming quite naturally that a virus was also a protein, tried to apply similar techniques to the purification of the virus. Unexpectedly, he found that a pure extract of the virus was crystalline. Moreover, these crystals, dissolved and applied to tobacco plants, produced the mosaic disease. Stanley had found a living crystal! Now it had been quite clear for some time that a virus could grow only inside living cells. Once inside them, it reproduced and behaved quite like a living organism. Yet outside the cell, it could be crystallized and would behave quite like a crystal, as if it were not alive at all.

Viruses are many times smaller than cells and it was only

with the invention of the electron microscope that they became visible. They have a structure and they have some of the essential properties of living things, certainly that of reproducing themselves—under proper conditions, at any rate. Their peculiar nature pointed to the possibility that viruses might provide a clue to the characteristics of those elements in chromosomes which are the ultimate hereditary units. Years before, after chromosomes had been established as the carriers of the hereditary factors, it became very clear to investigators like Sutton and others that the number of inheritable characteristics so greatly exceeded the number of chromosomes that each chromosome must carry many factors at least as small as viruses. In 1909 the Danish biologist Wilhelm Johannsen (1857–1927) called these factors "genes," and the particular configuration of genes an organism possessed, its genotype. Precisely what a gene might be was by no means clear. It was defined as the physical basis of a hereditary trait, and though it could not be seen and its nature was unknown, it turned out to be a very fruitful concept and much important work was done in terms of it. As we shall see, the work on viruses that Stanley initiated came to illuminate the nature of genes, but we should first consider what was learned about genes even before anyone knew precisely what they were.

The American geneticist Thomas Hunt Morgan (1866–1945), perhaps more than any other single person, brought classical genetics to a high state of development. In the course of his initial researches he sought an appropriate experimental animal and, out of thousands of possibilities, hit upon the fruit fly *Drosophila melanogaster*. With both high intelligence and a bit of luck, he picked the right organism, and no single creature has taught us more about inheritance than the fruit fly. What were its advantages? It was small and easy to handle, it bred rapidly (you could get a new generation every two weeks), and it produced fairly large numbers of progeny from one mating. All this was intelligence on Morgan's part. His luck came in because of the fact that *Drosophila* could be used successfully in experiments in sex determination. It was found out later that many organisms possessing *Drosophila's* other advantages would have been much more difficult to study in this respect. Since it had giant chromosomes in the salivary glands of its larvae, it could also be used to elucidate the relations between chromosome structure and genetic change. This too was an advantage not initially perceived.

Morgan began work on *Drosophila* in 1907. De Vries's great work on mutations, however problematic his results later proved to be, had directed the attention of geneticists to the problem, and Morgan's first studies with fruit flies were studies in their mutations, the first such investigations undertaken with animals. With the revival of genetics, two British geneticists, William Bateson (1861–1926) and R. C. Punnett (1875–), showed in 1906 that not all traits obeyed the Mendelian law, and Morgan's researches were extended to this problem. For several years he exhaustively investigated the phenomena of "linkage," those traits inherited together which did not segregate or assort themselves independently. It was clear that these were the traits carried on a single chromosome and that there were many of them. Morgan was completely convinced that Sutton's hypothesis was correct, that genes are on chromosomes and that linked traits occur because the genes for those traits are on the same chromosome. Morgan was also convinced—though the evidence for this was not very abundant at the time—that genes were physical structures, particulate in nature and, in theory at least, capable of being located. In the state of knowledge of the time, it was quite conceivable that, whatever a gene was, it might be the result of several unknown and perhaps discrete entities working together to determine a single trait. Morgan's hypothesis proved to be an admirable working hypothesis, but it soon presented him with a remarkable problem.

Linked traits inherited together would suddenly "separate," be inherited separately. If the chromosome theory of inheritance, as it had been developed, was correct, there was nothing to do but assume that genes were mobile, that they might pass from one chromosome to another. A good many workers were not ready to believe this and some were even prepared to question the experimental data of the linkage studies. The answer came from some researches undertaken by a cytologist, F. A. Janssens (1863–1924), between 1905 and 1909. Janssens was very much interested in the phenomena of meiosis and made careful studies of synapsis and "crossing over." First, let us recall that in the prophase of meiosis the chromosomes first appear as single-stranded, unlike the case in mitosis, where each chromosome is composed of two chromatids from the very start. After their formation in meiosis as single-stranded chromosomes, the homologous pair with each other in synapsis, that is, they come together along their lengths. Following synapsis, the chromosomes duplicate while still together, each single-stranded chromosome becoming a double-stranded chromosome composed of two chromatids. A "tetrad" of four chromatids is thus the result, two of one homologue and two of the other. They then begin to pull apart but remain connected at various points for a while. Janssens noted that at this stage the chromatids seemed to wrap themselves around their homologues at one or more points, and that sometimes a chromatid of one pair would break at the same place as a chromatid of another pair. Janssens suggested that the broken pieces rejoined, but did not necessarily rejoin with the original chromatid. Since the pieces were of equivalent size, the chromatids might, in effect, exchange pieces. And as one pair of chromatids, one chromosome, is derived from one parent and the other from the second parent, there could, through this crossing over of chromatid segments, be a transfer of genes from one homologue to another.

Janssens had tentatively suggested that this process had genetic significance, but it was Morgan who clarified what that significance could be. The separation of linked genes was a consequence of one gene remaining on a chromosome and the other crossing over to that chromosome's homologue. Cytological proof was not obtained of the genetic significance of crossing over until 1931, about twenty years after Morgan and his coworkers had advanced their theory, but the hypothesis permitted Morgan and his successors to account for the phenomena associated with linkage without scrapping the very strong evidence which supported the conception that genes occupied fixed places on specific chromosomes.

It is interesting that Morgan's group of workers advanced the possibility of the crossing over of genes before they had come across Janssens' work. Even Janssens' hypothesis was tentatively formulated, since it is quite impossible to see the process of crossing over actually take place in living material. One can only infer from stained material that chromatid segments might actually have been exchanged. In this brief sequence we have a brilliant example of how theoretical necessity led to a hypothesis, how some conjectural evidence provided the first support for it, and how indirect and mounting evidence sustained it until it could actually be demonstrated. Later studies on *Drosophila* in which visible chromosomal abnormalities were found linked to particular genetic traits gave the appropriate material for demonstrating that crossing over actually occurred. Segments of peculiarly shaped chromosomes with known genetic characteristics were actually seen to have been exchanged in *Drosophila* crossings in which linked characteristics separated. That is, morphologically distinguishable chromosome segments known to carry specific genes were actually detected as having crossed over.

One result of the studies of linkage was to be of momentous significance for genetics. Linked traits were found to separate in constant percentages. While the percentage varied in the case of any two genes, it remained constant for any specific pair. If, as seemed to be the case, genes occupied fixed places along the chromosome length, this meant that the breaks in the chromatid strands which occurred during crossing over were not simply "accidental" occurrences. But even more important, the percentage of "separation" or crossing over of normally linked genes would be proportional to the place of the gene along the length of the chromosome. For one thing, all percentages of "unlinking" or crossing over varied between less than one percent to almost but not quite fifty percent. It was clear that the longer the distance between two genes on a chromosome the greater the chance that crossing over would separate them. If they are close together, on the other hand, the chances of their remaining together when a bit of chromatid is exchanged are much greater. The linked genes, therefore, which were far apart unlinked more often than those close together. The frequency with which crossing over or unlinking occurred would indicate their *relative* positions along the length of the chromosome.

These data and deductions from them enabled geneticists to construct "maps" of genes showing their relative positions along a line representing the chromosome. This remarkable achievement was the work of one of Morgan's most distinguished students, A. H. Sturtevant (1891–), who began to map genes in 1913.

The achievements of Morgan, his co-workers and his students left genetics the most beautifully organized and systematized branch of modern biology. Moreover, all of this remarkable work on heredity was accomplished without anyone knowing precisely what a gene was. The first clue concerning the nature of genes came with the work of another of Morgan's students, Hermann Muller (1890–1967). Muller was especially interested in mutations, but unfortunately for the investigator, they don't occur as often as one might wish who wants to study them. It seemed desirable to try to accelerate the production of mutations, and Muller found that both heat and X-rays would increase the rate of mutation. Other investigators used chemical "mutagens" in order to produce mutations for study. It came to seem probable, as one result of these investigations, that the changes which were reflected in mutations were very likely at a molecular level. More and more evidence accumulated that many genes affected even one simple character, such as eye color in *Drosophila,* and a single chromosome probably contained so many genes that they had to be submicroscopic in size. It was conjectured that they might be about the size of virus particles.

Chemical analysis of purified viruses showed that they were proteins but proteins of a special type, a nucleoprotein made of protein in combination with a nucleic acid. This is exactly the same sort of combination which makes up chromosomes and which had first been discovered as early as 1869 by the Swiss chemist Friedrich Miescher (1844–1895) in the nuclei of cells. Soon after Miescher's discovery, a German chemist, Albrecht Kossel (1853–1927), analyzed the nucleic acids and found that they contained phosphoric acid, a sugar later identified as of two types, ribose and deoxyribose, two nitrogen compounds called purines which he named adenine and guanine, and three nitrogen compounds of another type called pyrimidines which he named cytosine, thymine and uracil. These are abbreviated by the first initial, A, G, etc.

Kossel had really analyzed two kinds of nucleic acids without quite realizing it, and it was not until the work of the American chemist Phoebus Levene (1869–1940) that nucleic acids were discovered to be of two types and their chemical structure further elucidated. It was Levene who showed that the sugar Kossel could not identify was really of two types, ribose and deoxyribose, and that one kind of nucleic acid had one type of sugar and another had the other type. Moreover the ribose nucleic acid (RNA) had A, G, C, U, and not T. Levene showed that the molecule of a nucleic acid of either variety was made up of sequences of three units, a phosphoric acid molecule, a molecule of the appropriate sugar, and one of the purines or pyrimidines. Each of these units of three he called a nucleotide, and the nucleic acid molecule is composed of a chain of these nucleotides much as proteins are made up of polypeptide chains, that is, of sequences of amino acids.

The nucleic acids turned out to have a relatively simple chemical constitution, and indeed, shortly after Levene's work, nucleotides of various kinds were synthesized. In some ways, this apparent simplicity of the nucleic acids delayed recognition of their crucial role in the mechanism of heredity. It was, of course, clear that those parts of the cell where nucleic acids were most heavily concentrated were precisely the parts where the hereditary factors were carried. Even Kossel himself had noted that the heads of spermatozoa, packed with chromosomes, were rich in nucleic acid and relatively poor in proteins. Indeed, what proteins were found there were of a simpler kind than those found in somatic cells. In spite of all these facts, the nucleic acids received little attention in the search for the chemical basis of heredity.

There were, on the face of it, good reasons for this. Proteins, after all, were frequently found in conjunction with other substances, so that the hypothesis that proteins were the chemical basis of heredity was not excluded by finding so much nucleic acid in the chromosomes. It was found together with protein. More important, granted the far simpler structure of nucleic acids as compared with proteins, it seemed unlikely that anything less complicated than a protein could be chemically complex enough to carry the enormous number of hereditary factors for making even a simple organism. Only the protein molecule seemed big enough to carry the burden of heredity, and it was supposed that it was the protein found in association with the nucleic acids which did the work.

As we shall see, even after it was clearly shown that the nucleic acids were the chemical basis of heredity, it took a lot of work to discover how they were put together with sufficient complexity of structure and function to account for the extraordinarily elaborate tasks they had to perform. It was not enough to know, even with great accuracy, the exact chemical constitution of DNA, for example. One had to know how the molecule was structured if it was to explain anything about heredity at all, and the first models offered for the structure of nucleic acids were chemically plausible but biologically unconvincing. Biological explanation as distinct from chemical explanation required an as yet unformulated structure.

In 1944 a remarkable discovery was made which turned attention back to the nucleic acids as the chemical basis of heredity, in spite of the presumptions against this hypothesis. O. T. Avery (1877–1955), an American bacteriologist, and his co-workers were studying the pneumococci, or diplococci as they have been renamed, the small round bacteria which are the cause of pneumonia. Before the days of antibiotics, the ravages of pneumonia were very great and the organisms causing the disease were intensively studied in laboratories about the world in the hope of finding a vaccine or a truly effective treatment. This organism had interesting properties which held out some hope for developing successful treatment of the disease. Normally, diplococcus is surrounded by a gelatinous capsule made of a polysaccharide, a substance much like the sort of carbohydrate which constitutes starch. Small chemical differences in the capsule accounted for different strains of diplococcus as they were identified through differing immunological reactions. Except for these differing reactions, the various strains of diplococcus seemed identical. When grown on artificial media, diplococci produced small, smooth colonies of a very characteristic appearance. At intervals, however, mutations appeared which lacked the capsules, and the colonies they produced would have a rough appearance because of the absence of the slimy capsule. The encapsulated normal type of this organism was called S, for "smooth," while the mutant strain lacking the capsule was called the R type, for "rough." Both of these types would breed true for generations, so that the R strain was a genuine mutant.

What was of great interest to medical bacteriologists about the R type of diplococcus was that it did not cause pneumonia. Only the S type, with its various immunologically distinguishable capsules, would produce the disease. Perhaps if a way were found to change the S type into the R type in a patient, the disease could be conquered. In the course of various experiments, Avery and his co-workers prepared an extract from a culture of the S type and added it to the R type. Then a remarkable thing happened. The R strain, as far as anyone could tell, simply turned into the S strain. R diplococci began making capsules and were pathogenic.

What had happened? Was this a mutation? Occasionally, although very rarely, the R strain would produce an S mutant. Perhaps the extract from the S strain acted like a mutagen. Analysis of the extract showed that it was a pure solution of nucleic acid and contained no protein. It seemed unlikely that nucleic acid would act as a mutagen, if only because it is so universal a constitutent of living things that there would be far more mutations than there are if it were a mutagen. Moreover, artificially produced mutations were much more numerous and, most important, unpredictable. The S-strain extract produced only one kind of change in the R strain and produced it repeatedly. It seemed clear that the nucleic acid of the S strain had changed the hereditary material of the R strain in a precise and predictable way. Moreover, it had changed it to the genotype of the organism from which it had been derived.

Meanwhile, the work that Stanley had begun on viruses had continued, and viruses turned out to be admirable experimental organisms for the study of the role of nucleic acids. It was learned that viruses had a core of nucleic acid, either DNA or RNA but not both, and that this core was surrounded by a coat of protein. Heinz Frankel-Conrat (1910–), an American chemist of German origin, was able to separate these two parts of the virus by chemical means (1955) and show (about 1957) that the protein portion was totally noninfective while the nucleic acid portion retained some of its capacity to cause disease. Clearly, the "vital" portion of the virus was its nucleic acid. Further work on viruses and bacteriophages—viruses which attack bacteria—showed that the nucleic acid of these invading organisms used the chemical machinery of the host cell to make more of themselves. A virus multiplied in a host cell, making its own kind of nucleic acid and its own kind of protein coat, as it were, taking over the host's apparatus for making such substances. Since the nucleic acid was the active part of the virus, it must be the part which contains the "instructions" for making more of its own chemical constitutents. Such "instructions" certainly did not come from the host.

While the work on viruses was progressing, chemists were further investigating the structure of nucleic acids. They were found to exist in far longer chains of nucleotides than had originally been thought. Their structure was thus revealed to be quite complex. Further elucidation of the structure of DNA, the nucleic acid which is the major constituent of chromosomes, came with the work of Erwin Chargaff (1905–), an American chemist of Austrian origin, in the late forties. Levene had thought that the purines and pyrimidines of the nucleic acids all existed in equal quantities so that in a sample of DNA, A, G, C and T would all be found in equal amounts. He also assumed that the nucleotides would arrange themselves in a uniform repeating series of four.

Chargaff showed that the relations between the purines and pyrimidines were more complex and more varied than Levene had thought. In any sample of DNA the amount of a particular purine, adenine for example, would equal the amount of a pyrimidine, thymine in this case. Moreover, the same would be true for the purine guanine and its corresponding pyrimidine, cytosine. While different kinds of DNA might have differing proportions of A and T relative to G and C, the proportions of A to T and G to C would be equal. Different kinds of DNA from different organisms would thus vary in their structure and in the *proportions* of their basic constituents, but certain proportions *between* these constituents were identical in any sample of DNA. It was clear that the DNA molecule was not everywhere identical, and that it could not be arranged in a simple repeating sequence of fours making identical tetrad units. It was also clear that the nucleic acids had the essential role in the chemistry of heredity, that they were chemically complex, and that they gave evidence of being both various and ordered. What structure would account for DNA's chemical properties and for the biological properties it was believed to have?

During the early fifties, a group of workers at Cambridge University, two Britons, M. H. F. Wilkins (1916–) and F. H. C. Crick (1916–), and one American, J. D. Watson (1928–), using X-ray diffraction data, attempted to work out the structure of the DNA molecule. The American chemist Linus Pauling (1901–) had suggested a helical structure for the protein molecule, and the Cambridge investigators thought that some modification of that structure would probably do for DNA. A double helix with a varying sequence of paired pyrimidine and purine bases, paired in the way Chargaff's analysis indicated and linked to a "double backbone" of phosphates and deoxyribose, would account for the available data. Moreover, this extraordinary "twisted ladder" would have the remarkable property of being a molecule which would replicate itself.

It was known that the amount of DNA in the nucleus of the cell duplicates itself just before the cell divides, and known for a much longer time that the chromosomes duplicate in the resting stage of the cell. Here on the molecular level was a unit, quite distinctly chemical, which replicated itself and which was complex enough to shape the processes that expressed hereditary traits. How did this molecule replicate itself? The backbone of the helix would unwind, and the two halves would build up their complements from the purines and pyrimidines present in the surroundings. A gene would be a segment of this long strand, and a mutation would be nothing more than a slight deviation in this process of self-replication. This remarkable achievement of the scientific imagination was published in a very short announcement, scarcely a few hundred words in length, in the British scientific journal *Nature* in 1953.

Heredity is manifested in particular physical traits. If this molecule was the very substance of heredity, as all the work on diplococcus and viruses seemed to show, how did one get from DNA to the actual structures of the cell? One important answer to this great question was latent in the work of George W. Beadle (1903–   ) and Edward L. Tatum (1909–   ), two American geneticists then working at Stanford University. In the attempt to find the biochemical consequences of mutation they selected for study a common variety of bread mold, *neurospora crassa,* and in 1941 began a series of experiments which would eventually win them the Nobel Prize. *Neurospora* had a number of very valuable properties in an experimental organism. For one thing it was haploid, that is, it had one set of chromosomes so that any mutation would immediately show up and not be masked by a gene remaining intact on the homologous chromosome of a diploid set of chromosomes. For another, it could grow on a very simple medium without any amino acids. In short, this simple mold could make all of the amino acids it required to manufacture the proteins and enzymes for its existence.

When these molds were exposed to X-rays, mutations were produced, and it was discovered that some of these mutants had lost the ability to make one or another amino acid. Such a mutant strain required the mixture of that specific amino in its medium if it was to grow. Any inability to make an amino acid is traceable to the lack of a specific enzyme required to manufacture the amino acid in question. There are various stages in the manufacture of amino acids and each one requires a particular enzyme to take place. The mutant mold could make one or another of the so-called "precursors" of the amino acid, but lacking a specific enzyme, it could not carry the process through to conclusion.

Beadle and Tatum concluded that a mutation in a gene, whatever a gene was, meant a change in the organism's capacity to manufacture an enzyme. They summarized their results in the phrase "one gene—one enzyme." Further work has modified this phrase to read "one gene—one polypeptide chain," that is, one gene controls the manufacture of a polypeptide chain, the particular long sequence of amino acids which is a fundamental constituent of any protein molecule, whether enzyme or not.

The work of Beadle and Tatum was the first conclusive demonstration that specific genes controlled specific stages in the process of protein synthesis. Genes had in effect been given a concrete biochemical definition, and biology had come that much closer to specifying their precise physical status.

Once the role of DNA as the genetic material itself was evident and its structure clarified, the new problem was to explain how DNA, which always remained within the nucleus, controlled the synthesis of proteins in the cytoplasm. The electron microscopy of cells had revealed very small bodies, first called microsomes and later, after George Palade (1912–) showed that they were full of RNA (1956), renamed ribosomes. These were suspected to be the sites of protein synthesis, and during the late fifties they were shown to be such. Now the genetic "information" in the DNA of the nucleus must get to the ribosomes and this, it was found, was accomplished by a nucleic acid of the RNA type called messenger-RNA. DNA not only makes more of itself but it also makes RNA of each of the types found in the cell. The messenger-RNA manufactured by the DNA of the nucleus is a complementary copy of segments of the DNA strand. This messenger-RNA travels out to the ribosomes. Considerably smaller molecules of RNA called transfer-RNA are also manufactured by the DNA of the nucleus. These, entering the cytoplasm, pick up specific amino acids and bring them to the matching places on the messenger-RNA at the ribosomes.

There are at least as many kinds of transfer-RNA as there are amino acids and the problem, in its ultimate form, was to figure out what the mechanism of specific attachment was. Since there are twenty amino acids, on the one hand, and only four bases, two pyrimidines and two purines, to each nucleic acid unit, the attachment could not be of an amino acid to one of the bases only or to one unit. At least three bases in one of the sixty-four possible triplet combinations of four types are required to specify or match up with an amino acid.

Not all of these combinations are necessary or actual. In theory only twenty are needed out of the sixty-four possibilities. This situation has set up a mathematical problem of the sort familiar to cryptoanalysts: out of sixty-four possible three-letter "words"—sequences in this case—pick out the twenty that make sense: actually match or "code for" the amino acids. It seems clear that more than one triplet can match an amino acid, and there are still a good many complexities to be unraveled. Biology is not as neat as cryptography. The laboratory investigations that are attempting to determine which of the triplet combinations of nucleotides or bases do in fact match the twenty amino acids are described as "deciphering" or "breaking" the genetic code. This analogy is useful, but if taken too anthropomorphically it will be more confusing than enlightening. This code will be cracked in the test tube and not by a priori mathematical calculations.

These developments in molecular biology have surely been

among the most brilliant in the entire history of the science of biology. Genetics and biochemistry have, in effect, been united. With the hindsight of today's vantage point, it all looks like an inevitable development from the work of Mendel. He placed the study of genetics on a scientific basis and gave ample evidence that there are units of heredity. As data provided by geneticists mounted, the units of inheritance were identified with obscurely defined entities called genes. These were finally shown to be some kind of minute physical structures located on chromosomes. They were finally located as particular segments of the DNA molecule controlling a particular stage in protein synthesis.

Astonishingly enough, the new discoveries have shown what a remarkable identity there is to the chemical basis by which the most diverse organisms carry all the data for reconstituting themselves from generation to generation. DNA is found as the chemical basis of heredity in all known organisms, with the exception of a few viruses which have RNA instead, an unimportant exception since the principle of operation of this nucleic acid is the same. Yet we must remind ourselves that these discoveries have left some of the most important biological problems unmodified or altered only to a small degree. Insofar as the unit of biological study is finally the whole organism, molecular biology has, as yet, little to say about *what* is inherited as distinct from *how*. That is, it throws little light if any on how, through the developmental process, a hereditary factor is expressed in the organism. The evolution of populations, the whole process of adaptation and natural selection, are great areas of biological inquiry, and the new molecular genetics has left them unmodified. Of course, as processes occurring on the molecular level of organisms are better known, such data will enter into the whole fabric of biological science and undoubtedly throw light in unexpected ways on various dark corners. The general result of all the growing knowledge of biochemical mechanisms is to show us how similar the most diverse living things really are in certain essential ways. Yet the diversity of life as well as its identity demands our understanding, and that will necessitate new concepts and methods of inquiry. The problem with which biology started, that of development, remains the great problem still. The related problem of the origin of life itself has begun to be investigated, and although the classical arguments over "spontaneous generation" are all dead, we are again compelled to consider how, in fact, life did arise, as it must have, from inanimate matter. The old experiments of Redi, Spallanzani and Pasteur closed the question pretty much so far as the earth as we find it goes. But the earth was not always the same as it is now. The very presence of life has profoundly modified its surface and its atmosphere. We are able to conjecture with a fairly high degree of probability what the primitive atmosphere of the earth was like. It is plausible that it was composed of hydrogen, ammonia and methane, and in 1953 Stanley L. Miller, an American chemist, performed a remarkable experiment. To pure and sterilized water he added, in a sealed container, an artificial atmosphere of hydrogen, ammonia and methane. This mixture was then circulated for a week past electrodes giving off an electric discharge equivalent to the effect of solar ultraviolet (the hypothesized primitive atmosphere, lacking oxygen, would not produce the ozone layer which shields the earth from ultraviolet). At the end of the week Miller found that the mixture contained a number of organic compounds, including a few simple amino acids. Since that time other organic substances have been synthesized in analogous fashion.

The door has opened on a new field of inquiry, the chemical evolution of the earth, the evolutionary history of molecules. To a much greater degree than was the case with organic evolution, this field is quite likely to remain conjectural for a long time if not forever. There are no fossil molecules, after all. Yet unless the laws of chemistry, whatever the ultimate status of a scientific law is, have changed over the aeons, the future will show some remarkable and fascinating reconstructions of the evolutionary history of the molecules which make up living matter.

The truly ultimate question of biology, the one which interests all men and not biologists alone, is the one the psalmist asked many centuries ago: What is man? Here biology passes into psychology, anthropology, the other social sciences and the humanities. Yet even here biologists have a great contribution to make. The new branch of biology called ethology, the study of animal behavior, is at the same time the oldest branch—man has always been interested in the habits of animals, after all. Here the important investigations of Konrad Lorenz, Kurt von Frisch and others have already shed fresh light on human behavior. Neither thought of some kind nor systems of communication nor maternal love is exclusively the prerogative of mankind, nor do such phenomena stand outside the regularities which govern all of nature. The prototypes of our most distinctive human traits exist elsewhere among living things. Yet if vitalism is dead, so is naive mechanism. Man's capacity to speak, to use language, to pass from an exclusively biological world to the world of culture, to use culture for his biological advantage (and, alas, disadvantage), is unique among living things. This is not to say that the scientific understanding of these phenomena, is in principle at least, beyond us. It is simply to say that we are so organized that living matter reveals properties and powers in mankind that do not exist in the same degree or even in kind elsewhere.

The picture of life that emerges from the centuries of progress in biology is one that excites our wonder. Life exists, to the best of our knowledge, only on a planet moving about a star, and under certain physical and chemical conditions which are by no means found on most if any other planets. Judging from the earth, it is confined to a thin "envelope" at the converging point of water, land and air. This biosphere is the site of the totality of living things. From one point of view this totality may be looked upon as a single, complex system for capturing and regulating the flow of energy, a system of increasing order in a larger system, the universe as a whole, moving, according to the second law of thermodynamics, toward a less ordered equilibrium which will eventually make any life at all impossible. At least, this seems to be what is happening in our part of the cosmos.

From still another point of view, the totality of living things may be viewed as constituting a hierarchy of levels of organization. The smallest are the molecules of a large size, sufficiently similar in all organisms to permit us to say that there is a chemical unity to living matter. Cells, larger and more complex systems of molecules, confer a structural unity on living things, and the concept of evolution reveals that they possess what we might call a historical unity. Organisms exist at a level of organization which encompasses the other, lower, levels of molecule and cell, and all organisms are related finally to the total biological and physical environment which surrounds them in a system of continual dynamic interaction.

As one views the system of living things, life is characterized on the one hand by an exquisite balance between continuity, achieved through an extraordinarily exact and stable mechanism of self-replication, and on the other hand by an equally remarkable power to vary itself through recombinations and alterations in the genetic material. When we reflect on the particular chemical and physical conditions necessary for life as we know it, on the fact that life had to be both stable and variable to come into existence and transform itself in such an extraordinary number of ways, we cannot be blamed for thinking that the odds against it all must be overwhelming. Yet what seems highly improbable viewed in an instant and as a result, seems almost inevitable given an appropriate and simple starting point, the properties of matter, and aeons of time.

BIBLIOGRAPHY

A brief list of books for further reading in the history of biology

1 / *History and Philosophy of Science*

Arber, Agnes, *The Mind and the Eye: A Study of the Biologist's Standpoint*. Cambridge, 1954 and 1964. A fine account of the nature of biological thought.

Beveridge, W. I. B., *The Art of Scientific Investigation*, rev. ed. New York, 1957.

Bury, J. B., *The Idea of Progress*. London, 1920. Repr. New York, 1960.

Clark-Kennedy, A. E., *The Art of Medicine in Relation to the Progress of Thought*. Cambridge, 1945.

Cohen, M. R., and I. E. Drabkin, *A Source Book in Greek Science*. New York, 1948. Repr. Cambridge, Mass., 1959.

Dampier, W. C., *A History of Science and its Relations with Philosophy and Religion*, 4th ed. Cambridge, 1947.

Gillispie, C. C., *Genesis and Geology: The Impact of Scientific Discovery upon Religious Beliefs in the Decades before Darwin*. Cambridge, Mass., 1951.

———, *The Edge of Objectivity: An Essay in the History of Scientific Ideas.* Princeton, 1960.

Hall, A. R., *The Scientific Revolution, 1500–1800.* New York and London, 1954.

Heath, A. E., ed., *Scientific Thought in the Twentieth Century.* London, 1951. New York, 1954.

Knobloch, Irving W., ed., *Selected Botanical Papers.* Englewood Cliffs, N.J., 1963. Original sources for the history of botany.

Kuhn, Thomas S., *The Structure of Scientific Revolutions.* Chicago, 1962.

Mason, S. F., *Main Currents of Scientific Thought.* London and New York, 1954. Reprinted as *A History of the Sciences,* New York, 1962. The best brief treatment of the history of science.

Mazzeo, J. A., *Renaissance and Revolution: The Remaking of European Thought.* New York, 1965; London, 1967. In paperback as *Renaissance and Revolution: Backgrounds to Seventeenth Century English Literature.* New York, 1967.

McKenzie, A. E. E., *The Major Achievements of Science,* 2 vols. Cambridge, 1960. Vol. 2 is a collection of readings from primary sources.

Nagel, Ernest, *The Structure of Science: Problems in the Logic of Scientific Explanation.* New York and London, 1961.

Shapley, Harlow, Samuel Rapport, and Helen Wright, eds., *The New Treasury of Science.* New York, 1965. A fine collection of good writing on science, old and new.

Singer, C. J., *A Short History of Scientific Ideas to 1900.* Oxford, 1959.

Taton, René, *Reason and Chance in Scientific Discovery,* trans. A. J. Pomerans. New York, 1962.

Toulmin, Stephen, *The Philosophy of Science.* London, 1953. New York, 1960.

———, and June Goodfield, *The Discovery of Time.* New York, 1965. On the "historicizing" of the sciences.

Waddington, C. H., *The Nature of Life: The Main Problems and Trends of Thought in Modern Biology.* London, 1961. New York, 1962.

Wiener, Philip, and Aaron Noland, eds., *The Roots of Scientific Thought.* New York, 1957. A collection of valuable papers which first appeared in the *Journal of the History of Ideas.*

II / *History of Biology*

Asimov, Isaac, *A Short History of Biology*. New York, 1964.

Bodenheimer, F. S., *The History of Biology: An Introduction*. London, 1958.

Dawes, Benjamin, *A Hundred Years of Biology*. London and New York, 1952. A historical survey of modern biology.

Gabriel, Mordecai, and Seymour Fogel, eds., *Great Experiments in Biology*. Englewood Cliffs, N.J., 1955. A selection from the primary sources.

Gardner, E. J., *History of Biology*, 2nd ed. Minneapolis, 1965.

Green, J. R., *A History of Botany, 1860–1900*. Oxford, 1909.

Locy, W. A., *The Growth of Biology*. New York and London, 1925.

Nordenskiöld, Erik, *The History of Biology. A Survey*, trans. L. B. Eyre. New York, 1928. Strong on biographical matters.

Rádl, Emanuel, *The History of Biological Theories*, trans. E. J. Hatfield. New York and London, 1930.

Rook, Arthur, ed., *The Origins and Growth of Biology*. Harmondsworth. Middlesex, 1963. A selection from primary sources.

Singer, C. J., *A History of Biology to the End of the Nineteenth Century*, 2nd ed. London, 1949. A standard work on the history of biology. Repr. London and New York, 1959.

———,and A. E. Underwood, *A Short History of Medicine*, 2nd ed. Oxford, 1962.

Sirks, M. J., and Conway Zirkle, *The Evolution of Biology*. New York, 1964.

Suñer, A. P., ed., *Classics of Biology*, trans. C. M. Stern. New York and London, 1955. A good selection of source material.

Taylor, G. R., *The Science of Life: A Picture History of Biology*. New York and London, 1963. Copiously illustrated.

III / *Anatomy and Physiology*

Bernard, Claude, *An Introduction to the Study of Experimental Medicine*, trans. H. C. Greene. New York, 1937. A classic of biological literature.

Clark-Kennedy, A. E., *Stephen Hales: An Eighteenth-Century Biography*. Cambridge, 1929. A study of the work of the pioneering plant and animal physiologist.

Chauvois, Louis, *William Harvey. His Life and Times, His Discoveries, His Methods.* New York and London, 1957.

Cole, F. J., *A History of Comparative Anatomy; from Aristotle to the Eighteenth Century.* New York and London, 1944.

Goodfield, G. J., *The Growth of Scientific Physiology.* London, 1960.

Harvey, William, *De circulatione sanguinis,* trans. K. J. Franklin. Oxford, 1958. Two letters to Jean Riolan known in Harvey scholarship under the above title. The volume includes other letters dealing with the circulation of the blood.

———, *Exercitatio anatomica de motu cordies et sanguinis,* trans. Robert Willis. London, 1847. Harvey's masterpiece, variously reprinted. The best translation, by K. J. Franklin, is available in the *British Medical Journal,* 1957, i, 1293.

Raven, C. E., *English Naturalists from Neckham to Ray.* New York and Cambridge, 1947.

Singer, C. J., *A Short History of Anatomy from the Greeks to Harvey.* New York, 1958.

IV / *Cytology*

Hughes, Arthur, *A History of Cytology.* London and New York, 1959.

Sharp, L. W., *An Introduction to Cytology.* New York, 1934. Ch. 26 is a brief history of cytology.

V / *Embryology*

Adelmann, H. B., *Marcello Malpighi and the Evolution of Embryology,* 5 vols. Ithaca, N.Y., 1966. A monumental study of Malpighi and the history of embryology with many primary sources.

Aristotle, *De generatione animalium,* trans. A. L. Peck. London, 1943. The first and in some respects greatest classic of the literature.

Cole, F. J., *Early Theories of Sexual Generation.* Oxford, 1930.

Meyer, A. W., *An Analysis of the De generatione animalium of William Harvey.* Stanford, Cal., 1936. A study of Harvey's embryological work.

———, *The Rise of Embryology.* Stanford, Cal., 1939.

———, *Human Generation: Conclusions of Burdach, Döllinger and von Baer*. Stanford, Cal., 1956.

Needham, Joseph, *A History of Embryology*. Cambridge, 1934. 2nd ed., Cambridge, 1959.

Willier, Benjamin H., and Jane M. Oppenheimer, eds., *Foundations of Experimental Embryology*. Englewood Cliffs, N.J., 1964. A collection of the classic papers in the field.

VI / *Evolution*

Barnett, S. A., ed., *A Century of Darwin*. Cambridge, Mass., and London, 1958. Anniversary essays assessing Darwin's work and its cultural as well as scientific influence.

Darwin, C. R., *Autobiography*, ed. N. Barlow. London, 1945. New York, 1958. Also available in other editions

———, *A Naturalist's Voyage Around the World in H.M.S. "Beagle"*. London, 1930. Also in other editions.

———, *Origin of Species*. 1859. Many editions of this momentous book are available.

Drachmann, J. M., *Studies in the Literature of Natural Science*. New York and London, 1930.

Eiseley, Loren, *Darwin's Century: Evolution and the Men Who Discovered It*. New York, 1958.

Glass, H. B., O. Temkin, and W. L. Straus, Jr., eds., *Forerunners of Darwin: 1745–1859*. Baltimore, 1959.

Huxley, Julian, *Evolution: The Modern Synthesis*. London, 1942. Repr. New York, 1964.

Irvine, William, *Apes, Angels and Victorians*. New York, 1955. A biographical study of both Darwin and Huxley.

King-Hele, Desmond, *Erasmus Darwin*. New York, 1964.

Lamarck, J. B., *Zoological Philosophy, An Exposition with Regard to the Natural History of Animals*, trans. H. Eliot. New York, 1963. A recent reprint of this long-unobtainable work.

Sears, P. B., *Charles Darwin: The Naturalist as a Cultural Force*. New York, 1950.

Simpson, G. G., *The Meaning of Evolution*. New Haven, Conn., 1949 and 1960.

Pearson, Hesketh, *Doctor Darwin*. New York, 1963.

VII / Genetics

Boyer, S. H., ed., *Papers on Human Genetics*. Englewood Cliffs, N.J., 1963. Primary source selections.

Dunn, L. C., *A Short History of Genetics*. New York, 1965.

Krizenecky, Jaroslav, ed., *Fundamenta Genetica: The Revised Edition of Mendel's Classic Paper with a Collection of Twenty-Seven Original Papers Published During The Rediscovery Era*. Oosterhaut, the Netherlands, and Prague, 1965. New York, 1965.

Mendel, Gregor. Translations of Mendel's paper are available in William Bateson, *Mendel's Principles of Heredity*, Cambridge, 1909 and 1913; in E. W. Sinnott, L. C. Dunn, and Th. Dobzhansky, *Principles of Genetics*, New York, 1950; and in slightly abbreviated form in the anthology by J. A. Peters cited below.

Moore, John A., *Heredity and Development*. New York, 1963. A distinguished college text in which the material is developed historically.

Morgan, T. H., *The Theory of the Gene*. New Haven, Conn., 1926. Repr. New York, 1964.

Peters, J. A., ed., *Classic Papers in Genetics*. Englewood Cliffs, N.J., 1959. Original sources.

Roberts, H. F., *Plant Hybridization before Mendel*. Princeton, 1929. Repr. New York, 1965.

Olby, R. C., *Origins of Mendelism*. London and New York, 1966.

Sturtevant, A. H., *A History of Genetics*. New York, 1965. A history of genetics by one of the most important of the men who helped make it.

VIII / Microbiology

Brock, T. D., ed., *Milestones in Microbiology*. Englewood Cliffs, N.J., 1961. Primary sources in selection.

Bulloch, William, *The History of Bacteriology*. Oxford, 1938.

Cole, F. J., *History of Protozoology*. London, 1926.

Curtis, Helena, *The Viruses: Their Role as Agents of Disease and as Probes into the Nature of Life*. New York, 1965. An excellent historical account of modern virology and molecular biology.

Dobell, Clifford, ed. and tr., *Antony van Leeuwenhoek and his*

"Little Animals." London, 1932. Repr. New York, 1962.
Dubos, R. J., *Louis Pasteur, Free Lance of Science.* Boston, 1950.
Hooke, Robert, *Micrographia.* London, 1665. Repr. New York, 1961.
Lechevalier, Hubert, and Morris Solotorovsky, *Three Centuries of Microbiology.* New York, 1965.
Schierbeek, Abraham, *Measuring the Invisible World: The Life and Works of Antoni van Leeuwenhoek F.R.S.* New York and London, 1960.

IX / *Microscopy*

Clay, R. S., and T. H. Court, *The History of the Microscope: Compiled from Original Instruments and Documents, up to the Introduction of the Achromatic Microscope.* London, 1932.
Gage, S. H., *The Microscope.* Ithaca, 17th ed. New York, 1943. Contains a brief history of lenses and microscopes.

Index

INDEX